Never give up on
your dreams

DayOne

© Day One Publications 2011

First printed 2011

Reprinted 2015

ISBN 978-1-84625-271-6

British Library Cataloguing in Publication Data available

Published by Day One Publications
Ryelands Road, Leominster, HR6 8NZ

☎ 01568 613 740   FAX 01568 611 473

email—sales@dayone.co.uk

web site—www.dayone.co.uk

☎ Toll Free 888 329 6630 (North America)

Designed by **documen**
Printed by TJ International

Dedication

To my twin granddaughters: Louise,
who originally inspired this story,
and Danielle, whose courage in coping
with disability is an example to us all.

My grateful thanks go to Malcolm,
my patient husband, who is always so encouraging.
I would also like to thank my publisher, Day One,
and especially Suzanne Mitchell for her help.

Chapter one

'Gabrielle, sit down and eat your breakfast!' said her mum in a voice that showed she was getting cross.

'Sorry, Mum,' replied Gabrielle as she sat herself down at the table. Her big brother, Paul, and little sister, Amy, had almost finished their breakfasts already.

Mum sighed deeply. What was she going to do with Gabrielle? She just couldn't sit still for five minutes at a time, let alone to eat a whole meal! Gabrielle was always bouncing around the house, doing cartwheels or handstands. She was never where she was supposed to be! Dad called her 'Tigger', as she was always bouncing somewhere! Mum wondered where she got all her energy from. Paul and Amy were both very active too, but nothing like Gabrielle!

The children finished their breakfasts and brushed their teeth, ready to go to school. As usual, it was a last-minute rush to make sure that all the children had everything they needed for the day. Paul needed his football kit and Gabrielle her swimming gear. Mum still walked to school with the girls as little Amy was just four years old and was in reception class; she proudly carried her book-bag and her

lunch-box. Gabrielle was six and was in Year 2. Paul was
ten and was in Year 6, so he was quite old enough to walk
on his own.

It was a sunny autumn morning, and, as usual, Gabrielle
let go of Mum's hand and started to scrunch through the
leaves that had fallen from the trees. Soon she was hopping
and skipping and having a marvellous time.

'If only I didn't have to go to school,' she thought to
herself. 'It would be such fun to play in the leaves all day!'
It wasn't that she disliked school, for she had lots of friends
there, but she hated sitting still and was always in trouble
for jumping up and down. 'Never mind,' she said to herself,
'today is swimming day, and that's fun!'

At the end of the day, Mum collected Amy first then
waited for Gabrielle to come out of her classroom. As she
appeared, Mum noticed that she was carrying a letter
and she gave a big sigh. Was Gabrielle in trouble again?
Too many letters had been sent home complaining that
Gabrielle would not sit still and pay attention to her work.

'A letter for you, Mum,' shouted Gabrielle as soon as she
spotted her mum waiting for her in the playground.

'So I see,' replied Mum, as she took the envelope and put
it into her handbag.

Once they were home, Mum gave the children some
milk and a biscuit, then put the kettle on to make a cup of
tea. She thought she might need that before she read the
letter from the school! But, when she opened the letter,
she saw that it was from the headmistress and, instead of
complaining about Gabrielle, the letter was praising her!
The headmistress explained that the swimming instructor
had been watching Gabrielle in the pool for some weeks

and felt that she was not merely good at swimming but had a real talent, which he felt should be developed! Then the letter asked if Mr and Mrs Price, Gabrielle's parents, would like to meet the instructor at the school and talk about how she could receive the best training possible!

Mum sipped her tea, looking at the letter on her lap. Then she noticed that Gabrielle was looking at her, rather worried in case she was in trouble again. Mum smiled at her. 'It's all right, love,' she said. 'This is just a letter telling us how well you're getting on in the swimming class. Your swimming teacher would like to have a chat with us. I'll talk to Dad this evening and we'll see when we can fix it up. Now,' she said, addressing all the children, 'it's time for you all to do some reading before I get your tea ready.'

As usual, Gabrielle pulled a face at this, but Amy ran to get her book-bag. Paul already had his nose in a book, because reading stories was one of his favourite hobbies.

About a week later, Mr and Mrs Price went to the school one evening to see the swimming instructor and the head mistress. Granny Price, who lived nearby, came to sit with the children while their parents were out. The children all loved it when Granny Price came, because she always had time to play games with them and she rarely told Gabrielle off for fidgeting!

When the instructor spoke with Mr and Mrs Price, they were really surprised to hear what he had to say. He thought not only that Gabrielle was a very good swimmer for her age, but also that she had the ability and potential to go to the very top!

'You mean that she could swim for Great Britain?' exclaimed Mrs Price.

'Yes, I do,' said the teacher. 'With the right training I think we could have a world champion, an Olympic medal-winner! Of course, she's still very young at the moment, but she has the sort of character and determination that really count. However, it will mean a huge commitment from you, and it will also be costly. I know you have two other children, and it can be hard on them if you have a specially gifted child. I want you to go home and talk it over together, and then I'll phone you in a week or so and you can tell me what you've decided.'

By the time Mr and Mrs Price arrived back home, the children were all in bed. It gave them time to talk with Granny Price about the talent that Gabrielle had for swimming, and about what it would mean for them all as a family if she took on extra coaching.

'I'm willing to help you when I can,' said Granny. 'You know that I can look after Amy and Paul, but it will be very hard for them if so much time and money are given to Gabrielle.'

'Yes, I know,' answered Dad. 'But first, I think we need to talk to Gabrielle and ask her if it is what *she* wants to do. After that, we can have a family conference and talk about the sacrifices we will all have to make. We do appreciate your offer of help, Mum; we couldn't do without it.'

And that is how it all began. Everyone in the family agreed that Gabrielle should have the chance to 'go for gold' and train to be the best swimmer she could be.

Chapter two

Two years had passed since Gabrielle had been spotted by the school instructor as having talent as a swimmer. She had worked very hard during those years. At first it was quite easy, because it only meant getting up very early on Saturdays, when Dad took her to the swimming pool at 6 a.m. and she worked with the trainer for two hours. How she enjoyed those sessions! She learned to swim well using every stroke and had races against other children who were also training. After a short time, she found she could win some of the races. Breast-stroke was her strongest stroke, and she began to win more and more as she raced against the others. It made her feel good and also spurred her on to work even harder in the training sessions. She also went to the pool several times during the week, but these times were for her to practise what she had been taught. Often, Granny Price would take her, and Gabrielle loved these times with her grandmother.

She found out that her grandmother was quite a good swimmer too, and they would enjoy racing against each other. Granny seemed to understand how hard it was for Gabrielle to sit still and concentrate on her lessons at school. Now that she was swimming so much, she was finding it a bit easier to sit still, as she had less excess energy—but often she felt too tired to do her work. Gabrielle talked to Granny about it one evening when they were driving to the pool, and Granny promised to pray about the problem. Gabrielle was not really sure what 'praying' meant, except that it was something to do with talking to God and it was something her Granny did. Maybe talking to God was what old people did, especially if they were sad sometimes, just as Granny had felt sad since Granddad had died.

One Saturday morning, Mr Black, the swimming coach, asked Gabrielle and her dad to stay behind after her training session and have a chat.

'You've just had your eighth birthday, I understand,' he said to Gabrielle.

'Yes—I'm Year 4 now,' she answered.

Mr Black looked at Dad and said to him, 'I think it's now time to increase Gabrielle's training schedule. She's doing very well, working really hard, and she shows she has real talent.

'I'd like her to start to train every morning before school. It won't be easy, because it means getting up very early and is a big commitment. Gabrielle has to be willing, and so do you or whoever will bring her.'

'Oh yes, I'll do it!' Gabrielle was dancing around with eagerness. 'We can do it, can't we, Dad?' she pleaded with her father, her eyes begging him to say 'yes'.

'How early is early?' Dad asked Mr Black.

'She needs to be at the pool at 5 a.m. each day, Monday to Friday.'

'5 a.m.!' exclaimed Dad. 'That means getting up at 4.30 every weekday!'

'Yes,' replied Mr Black, 'I'm afraid it does. I want you to think about it and give me your answer next week. It's no good starting if you can't keep it up. But, Gabrielle, if you want to one day swim in the Olympic squad, then you have to be willing to do it.'

Dad was very quiet in the car going home. Gabrielle didn't notice because she was so excited. It was all she could do to keep her seat belt done up and not jump up and down in the car. She knew she could do it! Of course Dad would make sure she was at the pool each morning! After all, she was going to be an Olympic star one day, and think how proud everyone would be then! Gabrielle never thought about how hard it might be for the rest of the family. She felt that she was special and deserved all the support and attention that were needed so that she could make her dream of winning a gold medal come true!

Gabrielle didn't realize how selfish she was becoming and how much all the family were sacrificing for her to achieve her ambition. Often she felt a bit tired and grumpy after a training session and she snapped at Amy, expecting her to tidy the bedroom they shared, always excusing herself by saying that she was special and training to be a swimmer! Amy was beginning to get fed up with being bossed around by her big sister. Paul was now in senior school and had lots of homework. He wanted Dad to help him sometimes and resented the fact that his sister had so much attention and he felt he had so little.

Dad was thinking about these things as he drove home. What should they do? He felt that it was time to have another family conference, because it would be hard on all of them if Gabrielle continued her training—but it would also be terrible for her if she had to give up now.

On Sunday, after tea, they all sat around the dining-room table, including Granny Price. Although she didn't say so out loud, Gabrielle was furious inside! There was no question in her mind. She was a gifted swimmer! Everyone knew that. She *must* be allowed to continue her training. The others would just have to put up with it and revolve their lives around her! They should be proud to have her in the family!

As they talked together, the grown-ups could see all the problems the swimming was causing the family. How could they give Gabrielle the chance and also not neglect Paul and Amy?

Granny had been doing her usual thing and praying about the situation. It was she who came up with an idea.

'Would Gabby like to come and live with me through the week? I can get up early and take her to the pool. After all, I can have a sleep in the afternoons, so I won't get too tired. I always wake up early anyway. That would mean that Dad doesn't have to get up early every day and struggle to get through his work at the office. Then you can all be together at the weekends.'

Everyone turned and looked at Granny Price. What a wonderful idea! Dad was worried, though. He didn't want his mum to get worn out, and this arrangement might have to go on for some years. Amy and Paul looked at each other and grinned. They didn't mind because Gabrielle had been grumpy to live with lately. They didn't have the fun together that they used to have before all this swimming business happened.

Gabrielle was beside herself, jumping up and down. Good old Granny! She always understood how important swimming was to her!

In the end, everyone agreed that Granny's plan was the best one.

'There will have to be some rules, though, young lady,' Granny said to Gabrielle.

'Anything, Granny! I promise I'll be good and helpful! I know I can make it. I know I can be a star!'

So it was all arranged and Gabrielle went to live with Granny Price. Every Sunday evening she walked down to Granny's house, and after school on Friday she went back home. At Granny's house she had a bedroom all to herself, and she loved it. It had once belonged to her Auntie Jenny, and it still had some of her books and one old doll that had been left behind. Gabrielle took quite a lot of her own things to the room, but she didn't take everything. She didn't want Amy to take over their bedroom completely!

She did miss having her sister in the same room. She missed being able to talk to her about things that had happened at school or swimming. She hadn't realized how good it was to talk to her sister, or how funny her sister could be and how often she made her laugh! She was also very surprised to find that she missed Paul. He had often answered her questions because he knew more than she did, and he helped her with her homework. She found herself thinking about what a nice brother he was! Of course, she missed Mum and Dad too, but she saw Mum at the school every day and gave her a big hug, and often, just before bed, she would either run back home to see Dad, or he would call in to give her a hug and ask about her training. Then, at the weekends, they all had a lot of fun together. Somehow, it was more fun than before she went to stay with Granny Price, because they had all missed one another so much.

Gabrielle's alarm went off at 4.30 every morning. She got used to the shrill noise and, because she was determined to be a champion, she made herself get out of bed straight away. She knew that, if she stayed cosy and under the duvet for even five more minutes, she would want to go back to sleep! Granny must have got up even earlier, because she was always already bustling about in the kitchen making a cup of tea. There was always a mug of steaming hot chocolate ready for Gabrielle before she grabbed her kit and they set off.

The first dive into the pool almost always sent shivers down her spine, but once she had swum a length or two, she was as warm as toast, even in the winter. Granny would sit in the stands and watch while Gabrielle went through her paces. Ten lengths breast-stroke, ten lengths front crawl; ten on her back, ten butterfly, front then back, then exercises, then instructions about improving her movements so that she moved strongly through the water, using as little energy as possible. How she loved the sensation of moving powerfully through the water! Sometimes she dreamed she was a plane flying through the sky! Other times she imagined she was a dolphin, especially when she was doing butterfly, which she found the hardest. Gabrielle never felt happier than when she was in the water.

One day, Gabrielle asked Granny if she got bored going to the pool every morning.

'Never,' said Granny Price. 'I love to watch you. I would have loved to be able to train to swim as well as you now do. In my day, we just didn't have the chance, especially girls. In those days, girls didn't have such good chances as boys, at least, not in ordinary families where there wasn't much money. There was a war going on as well, so many pools were closed to save money. Anyway, I bring my Bible with me and read a bit each day while you swim. Then I pray about the day and for all my family. That includes you, of course!'

When they got home after the training session Granny always cooked a wonderful breakfast for Gabrielle. After swimming she always felt so hungry and gobbled down the bacon, egg and baked beans as soon as they were put in front of her. Granny laughed and told her that she needed to eat very well to build her muscles. At night they often had pasta dishes, which Gabrielle loved. Very soon it was obvious that Gabrielle and Granny had become very special friends. It seemed that her life had a nice smooth pattern, even though it meant getting up so early every day and also going to bed long before her friends. School-work seemed, strangely, to become easier, because she was calmer.

In her class, Gabrielle was very popular. She had lots of friends and was not often grumpy now. When it came to sports, she was always chosen for the teams, because she was so fit and strong. Every time she went in for a competition her schoolfriends wanted to know about it, and they were always pleased if she did well. If it was a big competition, the headmistress would announce it to the whole school at assembly. It made her feel very proud and important, and even more determined that she would get to the top.

Chapter three

Gabrielle had been training for almost a year and her coach was delighted with her progress. Then, one day, things started to go a little wrong.

'Hi, Gabby,' called her best friend Paula, as Gabrielle entered the school gate one morning. 'I've got an invitation for you to come to my birthday sleepover!'

'Oh, thank you!' replied Gabby. 'That will be fun!' She put the letter into her backpack to show to Granny and Mum later. The two girls went off arm-in-arm as the bell rang, and they lined up to go into their class.

After school she saw Mum and Amy waiting to walk home with her, and she ran over and gave them both a hug. Then she remembered the letter.

'I've got an invite to Paula's sleepover party, Mum,' she said, diving into her backpack for the letter.

'Wow! That sounds great fun! You deserve a treat; you've been working so hard. When is it?' replied Mum.

'I don't know,' said Gabby as she tore open the envelope. Her face fell as she looked at the invitation. 'Oh, it's not at a weekend—it's a Tuesday night.'

'Oh, I'm so sorry, sweetheart,' said Mum. 'But you know

the rules. You can't go out during the week; you have to keep up the training.'

'It's not fair!' shouted Gabrielle. 'I go every morning to train. Surely it won't matter if I miss just once! Paula's my best friend!'

'I know, dear, but you can't go out in the week—that's the deal. You can ask Paula to come and have a sleepover with you any weekend you like, and we'll make sure it'll be a great weekend.'

'It won't be the same,' said Gabrielle angrily, and she stomped off down the road to Granny's house, not even bothering to say thank you to her mum for her offer.

As she went she thought to herself, 'I'll persuade Granny and get her on my side. She always understands and she'll let me go.'

But when she talked to Granny Price, she said exactly the same as Mum had done. Gabrielle sulked all through her tea and was really horrible to Granny. When it was bedtime she couldn't get to sleep because she felt so angry. She began to think how she could go to the sleepover. There must be some way!

Suddenly, she knew! She felt bad because it would mean being deceitful, but she was determined to go to Paula's treat.

As Paula's birthday drew nearer, Gabrielle made her plans very carefully. She told Paula that she would come to her party and sleepover, but she would be late arriving, and she would have to get up very early and creep out of the house in order to go to her training session.

'That's OK,' said Paula, 'just so long as you can come for some of it. You're my best friend and I so want you to be there!'

'I won't miss it, I promise!' replied Gabrielle. 'I'm really glad that you're my best friend!'

'When you're famous and you win a gold medal, I'll be there to watch, and I'll tell everyone that you're my best friend!' was Paula's answer.

Paula loved drawing and painting, so Gabrielle knew exactly what she would like as a birthday present. There was no problem with buying that. She emptied her money box and asked Mum to take her shopping on the Saturday morning before Paula's birthday. Mum was very happy to do that and helped Gabrielle choose a huge box of water-colour pencils that contained every colour you could imagine. They also bought some pretty wrapping paper and a card.

'I'm proud of you, Gabby!' said Mum. 'You were so upset at not going to the party sleepover, but you've stopped making a fuss.'

Gabrielle felt her cheeks burning. She hoped Mum wasn't looking at her. She hung her head a little and mumbled, 'Well, it's OK, Mum. We'll ask Paula to our house one weekend, like you said.'

Gabrielle felt ashamed when she thought of what she had planned. She didn't really want to be so naughty, but it wasn't fair that she had such a strict life. After all, one night away wouldn't hurt!

The night of the birthday Gabrielle told Granny that she was a little tired and wanted to go to bed a bit earlier.

'Are you feeling all right, dear?' asked Granny anxiously. 'You don't have a tummy ache or headache, do you?'

'No, Granny, I'm fine. I just feel a bit tired. We played a lot of netball at school today,' replied Gabrielle.

She went upstairs and got her swimming bag. In it were her costume, goggles, towel and bottle of water, ready for the morning. She added her pyjamas and toothbrush and Paula's present. Inside, she didn't feel very excited, but actually rather ashamed of herself.

She got into bed, setting her alarm clock for half an hour earlier than usual, then she read for a while until she heard Granny getting ready to come up to bed. Then she put her book away and pretended to be asleep when Granny popped her head around the door to check her, as she always did. Then Gabrielle waited until she knew Granny had fallen asleep. She heard her snoring gently, so she slid out of bed very quietly, picked up her bag and dressed in her party clothes. Finally, she put on her anorak. Carrying the bag in one hand and her shoes and torch in the other, she tried to creep downstairs without making any noise. At one point, the stair creaked and Gabrielle froze, holding her breath. Would Granny wake up? There was still the sound of gentle snoring coming from the bedroom, so she continued downstairs and through the hall and kitchen to the back door. To open the bolts, Gabrielle had to climb onto a stool, but she had practised this before, so did it quietly and easily. Then she unlocked the door, shut it carefully behind her, locked it again and put the key in her pocket. Her plan was to let herself back in before Granny woke at 4.15 a.m., so hopefully no one would know she had been out all night! It seemed such a simple plan once Gabrielle had thought it out.

Up the garden path she went, glad that Granny slept in the front and not the back of the house. She clicked open the gate and then began to run down the alley into the road.

It wasn't all that late, as she and Granny had to go to bed so early, but it was very dark! Gabrielle was feeling a little scared by now. She had never walked down the road in the dark on her own, and she felt afraid. Suddenly she heard a noise, and she stood still, her heart thumping loudly in her chest.

'What was that?' she thought, remembering stories she had heard of bad people who walked out at night. Then she breathed a sigh of relief as she saw it was just a cat trying to get into a black binbag. She walked on a bit further, and then she saw a group of young people walking towards her. The boys whistled at her as she passed, and she felt very frightened. She tried to walk on calmly, as if she did this every night, but as soon as they were out of sight she ran, and she didn't stop until she got to Paula's house.

There were balloons hanging on the gate and the house looked bright and cheerful. Gabrielle could hear the noise of the CD-player, and she hoped Paula would hear her when she rang the doorbell.

'Oh, come in,' said her friend. 'I was hoping you would soon be here. We're just going to eat!'

Once inside, Gabrielle felt more cheerful, and she got out her present for her friend. Paula loved her gift, just as Gabby had known she would.

'You look gorgeous,' she said to Paula, who was twirling around in a new black-and-red skirt.

'You look good, too!' her friend answered. 'Come on, don't miss any more fun!'

They went arm-in-arm into the dining-room and Gabrielle saw that lots of her schoolfriends were there, as well as all Paula's family. The table was full of all the special party food that she was not normally allowed to eat, because of her special diet which was part of her training regime. Her eyes danced! How glad she was that she had come! She was sure that one night wouldn't make any difference! She began to eat crisps and sausage rolls, chocolate cakes and popcorn! Wow, was it good!

They had a kind of mini-disco, dancing in the lounge. Soon Gabrielle began to feel a bit sick; she wasn't used to eating so much party food. She decided to sit and watch the others dancing.

Paula's mum came over.

'Are you all right, Gabby?' she asked. 'You look a little pale. I could ring your mum and get her to take you home if you don't feel well. I know you have to get up early every day.'

'I'm fine, honestly,' Gabrielle replied very quickly, dreading the thought that they might call her mum. If that happened, she would be in trouble with a capital 'T'.

So Gabrielle decided she had better get up and dance anyway, to prove she was fine. She was very glad when the music stopped and they all sat down to watch a DVD.

Many of the girls were looking a bit tired by now, and Paula's young brothers had already been put to bed.

'I think it's time for bed!' said Paula's mum. It was half-past ten! 'Up you girls go and get ready, and we'll make the lounge ready for you.'

Soon they were all in their pyjamas and had cleaned their teeth. There was a lot of giggling as they all went downstairs again, for they were going to sleep on the lounge floor on mattresses. Gabrielle had her bag near her and she asked to be near the door, as she had to get up and slip out early.

She shyly asked Paula how to unlock the front door. She was a bit afraid to say anything to Paula's mum and dad.

'Are you going to go home alone at that time?' asked Paula. 'Surely your dad will come for you. I'll ask my dad to let him in.'

'Oh no, don't do that!' said Gabrielle quickly. 'I'll just slip out—don't worry. Dad will wait for me outside!' she lied. She hadn't thought about what it would be like going back to her grandmother's at that time of the morning; she had only really thought about getting to the party. When she thought about her parents and grandmother, she felt very uncomfortable and wasn't so sure that this adventure had been such a great idea after all. She was even less sure when she discovered that she had forgotten to pack her alarm clock! Gabrielle decided that the only thing she could do was to try to keep awake until everyone was fast asleep, and then to creep out and go home. She was very frightened at the thought of walking around the streets alone, but she knew she had to get out of the mess she had got herself into, one way or another.

Soon most of the girls seemed to have gone to sleep, but Paula was excited and kept whispering to Gabrielle. In the end, Gabrielle couldn't help herself—she fell asleep too.

The next thing she knew was the sound of voices in the hallway. She could hear her dad's voice; although he was talking quietly, she knew he was angry. Granny was there too—crying.

With a start she remembered all that had happened and where she was. She must have overslept! Oh, now there would be trouble!

The lounge door opened and Paula's mum came in. She

looked round and saw that Gabrielle was awake.

'Come quickly, your dad is here!' she said. Gabrielle could tell she was not happy, and she felt herself go red with shame.

She collected her things and she, Dad and Granny left the house.

Dad put her in the back of the car, and Granny sat in the front.

'What have you to say for yourself, my girl?' he asked sternly.

Gabrielle looked at his worried, angry face, and then at Granny's. Granny looked old, tired and very upset.

'I'm really sorry,' Gabrielle said. 'I just wanted to go out for once. It's not fair—Paula is my best friend, and it was her party!' Gabrielle felt so bad about her behaviour, she still felt sick and she was very tired.

'When Granny got up and found you weren't there, she was terribly worried, and when she rang me, I was too. Anything could have happened to you, walking out alone at night. Then it came to us that it was the night of Paula's party, so we guessed where you might be. So we had to disturb Paula's parents, who had no idea that you weren't allowed to be at the party. Since then, we've had your coach on the phone, wondering where you were.

'We'll need to have a serious talk about this, but now is not the time. I'm taking you home and you will get ready for school. After school today you will come home with Mum, and when I get home from work we'll talk about this party and see what is the best way to make you understand how deceitful and naughty you've been!'

'Yes, Dad,' sobbed Gabrielle, realizing that she was in

deep trouble. What had seemed to be such an adventure had ended up a nightmare.

At school that day, Gabrielle was very quiet. Paula knew that something was wrong, but she thought it was just the fact that her friend had overslept and missed her training session.

At break-time she put her arm around her friend and tried to cheer her up.

'You'll always be my best friend,' Paula said, trying to comfort her. 'I'm so glad you were allowed to come to my party!'

These words made Gabrielle dissolve into tears. 'That was the trouble—I wasn't allowed!' she sobbed. 'I ran away from Granny's to come, and she woke up to find my bed empty ... Granny was so frightened and upset. I feel terrible about it now. I didn't mean to upset everyone, I only wanted to be at your party!

'I'll need to talk to my mum and dad tonight—I'm afraid they'll be terribly cross. Why am I so naughty?'

The bell went, and the girls had to go back into class. Paula gave Gabrielle a tissue to blow her nose and wipe away her tears. She didn't know what to say to her friend. She only knew that she had got into trouble just so that she could be at her party. Gabby really was a best friend!

The day dragged by slowly. Gabrielle felt worse and worse as going-home time drew near. She was the last to get her coat, and for once in her life she had to be told off by her teacher for dawdling!

Mum was waiting at the school gate with Amy, who was chattering brightly to her friend. When Amy saw Gabrielle, she dropped Mum's hand and ran over to hug her sister.

'Isn't it nice that you're coming home for tea with us today!' she exclaimed.

Gabrielle didn't quite know what to say, so she muttered 'yes' softly. She didn't want to look at Mum's face, so she took hold of Amy's hand and started to walk home with her.

'Haven't you got a hug for me?' asked Mum. That made Gabrielle look at Mum; she could see that her eyes were red, as if she had been crying.

'Of course, Mum,' Gabby replied, and she went over and gave Mum a hug. It was so good to feel Mum's strong arms around her, and somehow to know that Mum still loved her, however cross she was.

'I'm so, so sorry,' she began to say, and the tears started once again.

'Never mind that now, sweetheart; we'll talk about it later. Let's go home and you can help me make tea. I'm sure Amy would like you to play with her,' said Mum.

At home, Gabrielle helped Mum get the tea ready, and then she went to play with Amy in their room. For once, she didn't mind playing Barbie dolls with her.

'I want to start ballet classes,' Amy told her sister. 'Daddy said I could if it fitted in with your training.'

'That would be nice,' Gabby replied. 'I think you'd be really good at dancing.'

She was trying to be extra nice to her sister. She thought about it for a few minutes and realized that she had never thought that it might be hard for Amy—or Paul, for that matter—to fit in the things they wanted to do because of her training. She had automatically expected everyone to fit in with her, as she was so 'special'. Once again, the tears felt very near the surface as she realized how selfish she was.

Soon Paul arrived home from school. He had been at an after-school chess club, and wanted to tell them all about the game he had been playing. He was a bit surprised to see Gabrielle at home, and he made a face when he heard that she had been helping cook tea!

'Suddenly I don't feel very hungry any more!' he teased.

Then Dad arrived home, and, rather shyly, Gabby went to give him a hug. In return she received a hug and kiss, and it made her hope that he wasn't quite so angry now.

At teatime they were all talking about their day, but Gabrielle kept rather quiet. She wasn't at all like her usual 'Tigger' self, but nobody seemed to notice. All too soon the meal was finished and she helped load the dishwasher. Paul went upstairs to do his homework, and Mum put a DVD on for Amy to watch in the lounge.

'Daddy and I need to talk to Gabby about her swimming training,' said Mum to the other two children. 'We'll be in the kitchen, but please don't disturb us for a few minutes. If the phone goes, just let it ring.'

This was the moment Gabrielle was dreading. Her heart was beating so loudly in her chest, she was sure everyone could hear it!

They sat down around the table. Gabrielle hung her head, not wanting to look at Mum or Dad because she felt so ashamed.

'Well,' said Dad, 'I guess we've all been dreading this all day! I know, just by looking at you, Gabby, that you are ashamed of your behaviour and sorry for what you did. We do need to talk about it, though. You see, your granny has given up such a lot to help you reach your goal of winning a gold medal in swimming. I don't know of many grandmothers who would do what she has done for you. She is not a young lady, and you gave her a terrible fright when she found you weren't in your bed. Also, you let yourself down by lying and deceiving us all. Was it worth it?'

'No, Dad,' said Gabrielle miserably, the tears beginning to seep out of her eyes again. 'I was frightened walking to Paula's in the dark, then I felt sick when I ate the party food, and then I was so ashamed of what I had done and the fuss I caused. I meant to wake up and go back to Granny's before she woke up.'

'It's just as well you did oversleep then,' chipped in Mum. 'Who knows what might have happened to you if you had walked home alone at that time in the morning!'

'I really am so sorry,' said Gabrielle again. 'I don't know what made me so naughty.'

'I think we need to talk about swimming,' said Dad. 'Is it really what you want to do? You don't have to carry on with training if you don't want to. However, if you decide it is what you want to do, then you must understand that you have to keep to the rules. Only people who have great determination and discipline will ever make it to the top of any sport.

'We all know you have great talent, but it takes more than talent to succeed.

'I've talked to Granny today. I wanted her to think again about her decision to look after you and help you. I wondered if it was too much for her, and somehow we would have to manage as a family if you decided to keep at it. But Granny was horrified at the thought of giving up helping! She loves you very much and, apart from last night, tells me you have been a very good girl. You know, she always wanted to swim to a high level herself but didn't have the chance like you have. She would hate to see you blow it, but none of us wants to force you into swimming at the top level. It has to be your choice.'

They were all quiet for a moment. Gabrielle really didn't need to take time to think; deep down, all she wanted was to swim and reach the top. She longed one day to win a gold medal. She would make them all proud of her!

'I really want to carry on swimming. I am sorry for what I've done. I will obey the rules and, one day, I will win a gold medal for you!' Gabrielle told them.

'But,' she continued, 'Amy told me she wants to do ballet. Please let her—don't let my swimming stop her.' It was the first time she had really thought about her sister wanting to do something; she was usually only thinking about her own needs.

'Don't worry about Amy, we'll do the best for her, and for Paul,' answered Mum. 'We just want a promise from you that from now on you will obey the rules.'

'Yes, I promise,' said Gabrielle.

'We had wondered what punishment to give you,' continued Dad, 'but when I saw your face this evening, I knew you had been punished enough. However, if you break the rules again, then there will be a severe punishment; probably we would stop the training.'

'Yes, Dad, but I won't break them again. I meant my promise!' said Gabrielle.

'OK. Now I'm going to walk you down to Granny's. You

need to say a big "sorry" to her. She is a wonderful granny.'

'I know,' said Gabrielle. 'Please can we stop at the garage and buy her some flowers? I've got enough money in my money box.'

'That sounds a very good idea,' said Mum, as Gabby raced upstairs to get her money box.

They bought a lovely bouquet of flowers and Gabrielle went in to give them to Granny. She started to cry as she gave them to her and told her how sorry she was for being so naughty the night before. Granny hugged her and told her that she was forgiven.

Then Gabrielle was sent up to bed, ready for her early start the next day.

Chapter four

The coach, Mr Black, saw a new determination in Gabrielle after the sleepover episode. She put every ounce of strength into her training sessions. As well as her early-morning sessions, he now put her in a special group which met twice a week after school. As she raced against the other children she felt a surge of exhilaration and a fantastic feeling if she won! In fact, she was winning more and more races, especially using breast-stroke. That was most definitely her strongest stroke.

The group had two divisions, and very quickly Gabrielle moved from the second division to the first. This group often took part in high-level competitions throughout the county.

Dad usually came to collect her after these sessions, on his way home from work. He was very proud of his daughter. One evening, Mr Black asked Gabrielle and her dad to stop and see him before they went home.

'I would like to put Gabrielle in for the British Junior Championships this year,' he said.

Gabrielle couldn't quite believe what she was hearing! It would be her first real chance to win a medal! She had won first place at the schools' championships for their town, and also from time to time she had won at county level, but to swim at national level! Why, it was like a dream come true!

Dad, too, seemed amazed and was lost for words for a while.

'It would mean a trip to Bath to train in the Olympic-sized pool at the university there,' continued her coach. 'That's probably where the trials and eventually the Championships will take place.'

'Bath!' said Dad. 'I've always wanted to take the children there, so maybe we could go through the half-term holiday. Would that be a good time?'

'Yes, that would work out well for me,' said Mr Black.

'I'll arrange leave from work and then get back to you,' replied Dad.

All the arrangements were made and Dad found them a place to stay in a village called Limpley Stoke, which was near Bath and the university campus. Everyone came, Granny included. For once, Gabrielle didn't have to get up so early or go to bed quite so early. They were staying in a cottage that looked down on the river. It was very peaceful and quiet. At the back of the cottage was a field in which black and white cows grazed. The children, used to living in a town, had never been so close to cows before!

Gabrielle was taken to the university campus, which was on the top of a hill in an area called Claverton Down, and while she worked hard with her coach, the rest of the family drove down the steep hill into Bath to do some sightseeing. Paul's favourite place was the Roman Baths. At school he had learnt a lot about the Roman Invasion of Britain and he loved going around the ruins.

Amy's favourite trip was to the Museum of Costume. She had thought it might be boring when Mum and Granny suggested taking her there, but in fact she loved seeing all the clothes which people had worn in the olden days. There was also an exhibition of the Queen's ball gowns, and they were so beautiful! So much nicer than her princess dressing-up dress!

Although the family were all doing really nice things while Gabrielle was training, she really didn't mind. She loved racing through the water and got very excited every time she knocked a second off her personal best time. Some of the students in the university were in the British squad, and she even got the chance to swim with them. They were astonished at how well this young girl, who was still only nine years old, was doing! They talked to her as if she was a grown-up, and she felt very proud and important. They talked about their training regimes, and how, although it was hard and they had to give up doing so many other things, it was all worth it! Some of them had taken part in the Commonwealth Games and the European and World Championships, and they spoke about the thrill of swimming for their country.

'One day, I'm going to do that!' Gabrielle told them, with her eyes sparkling with excitement.

'Go on working hard and, if you want it badly enough, you will!' one of the students told her. Gabrielle vowed to herself that she would! She put every ounce of energy and determination into her training sessions that week.

There was one family outing which Gabrielle was able to join in, and she loved it! Granny had taken to having a walk along the canal bank early in the morning. In

Limpley Stoke, there was not only a river, but also a canal.
The weather was warm and fine, and Granny loved to
walk slowly along the path. One morning she came back
having seen a kingfisher, and she was excited about that.
Another day, as she walked along, a narrowboat chugged
slowly down the canal. It moored up near to where she
was walking, and she stopped to watch. The owner of the
boat cheerily called out 'good morning' to her, and Granny
answered him, commenting on how lovely the weather was.

'My wife's just brewing a pot of tea,' the man said.
'Would you like to join us for a cup?'

As he said this, a lady came out of the cabin and told
her husband that the tea was ready. When she saw Granny
Price standing there, she invited her to come in and see the
boat and join them for some tea.

Granny was a bit hesitant about stepping onto the boat,
but the couple took her hand and helped her in. It was so
cosy on the boat; Granny couldn't help herself saying, 'Oh,
wouldn't my granddaughters love to see this!'

As they had their tea and chatted together, Granny
learnt that the husband was working on the Kennet and
Avon canal as a chaplain to all the people who lived on
boats. 'Live aboards', they called them. Granny told the
couple that she, too, was a Christian, and she told them
about her family and why they were at Limpley Stoke for
the half-term holiday. They were getting on so well together
that Granny completely forgot the time!

'My goodness!' she exclaimed, 'I must get back or they'll
send out a search party for me, thinking I've fallen into
the canal!'

'Why don't you come back this afternoon?' the wife,

Jane, said. 'Bring all the family—we could take them for a trip up the canal and over the aqueduct.'

'Really?' said Granny, amazed at the kindness of her new friends. 'I'll check with my son, and if nothing else has been planned, I'm sure they'd all love to come.'

Jane and John helped Granny off the boat and she hurried back to the cottage to share the invitation with her family.

So it was that, after Gabrielle had finished her swimming, they all went for a walk along the canal and met Granny's new friends. The children were very excited about being able to go out on the boat. They took it in turns to help John to steer. As they travelled slowly (less than four miles per hour, John said), they saw some of the wildlife that lived on the canal bank. One swan kept coming and pulling a rope which was tied to a bell, and Jane gave the children bread to feed it. They listened to the mewing sound that the buzzards made as they circled above. It was so different from their life in their home town.

They slowly chugged across the aqueduct and looked down, amazed at a canal crossing a river. Paul took some photos, as he had his own camera. Jane had baked some cakes and cookies for their tea, which they all enjoyed very much.

Dad and John seemed to hit it off straight away, and soon John was being told all about Gabrielle and her swimming talent. John seemed really interested. He knew that Bath University was renowned for its sports faculty. He suggested that, when it was time for Gabrielle to change schools, she should come to senior school in Bath. She only had one further year to do at primary. John began to tell

Dad about a very good boarding school not very far from the campus. It was a school with a Christian foundation and had a very good reputation.

Secretly, Dad knew that they couldn't afford to send their daughter to a boarding school, but it was an interesting thought! But it would not be many weeks before they had to select a senior school for her, and not all schools would understand about her swimming.

The visit to the canal-boat had been a great success. Dad and Mum had so enjoyed being with Jane and John, making friends with them just as Granny had done. They exchanged postal and email addresses in order to keep in touch. It had been a wonderful trip, and Gabrielle had especially enjoyed doing something with all the family.

All too soon the week was over, and they had to pack up and go home. 'All good things must come to an end,' laughed Dad when he saw their long faces. 'We've had a great time, let's just be thankful! I think we'll probably come back again sometime so Gabby can train at Bath.'

'I'm glad you're a swimmer!' said Paul to his sister. 'I've loved coming to Bath. I wouldn't mind living here!'

'Now there's a thought!' said Mum.

Gabrielle just smiled to herself, glad that it had been such a good week for them all.

Chapter five

*B*ack at home they soon settled down into the usual routine. It was the summer term and there were lots of fun things happening. School sports day was one, and when it arrived it was a bright summer's day. Dad had taken a day off work and so he came along with both Mum and Granny to watch the girls in their races. Amy did well; they all cheered her on as she won the skipping race for her class and her team won the obstacle race.

Gabrielle also ran in the flat race for her class; she came first, and her relay team came second. She and Paula ran together in the three-legged race, but they fell over when they were almost at the tape. They got in such a muddle that, instead of being angry, they both began to giggle. They finally got up and giggled all the way to the finish! Mum and Dad both ran in the parents' races, and the girls clapped and cheered them on. It was all a lot of fun.

There were class outings that term, too. Gabrielle's class went to the Museum of London Docklands and, much to her surprise, she found it very interesting, especially the exhibition on the slave trade and the history of its abolition.

One thing Gabrielle was sad about was that she was not able to go to France with her year group. Paul had gone when he was in Year 5 but, because of her swimming training, Gabrielle wasn't able to go. She tried to be grown-up about it and not mind too much because of her promise to her parents that she would be committed to her swimming, but she did feel sad and also very lonely at school, as almost everyone else in her class had gone. She missed Paula especially, and even the postcard she sent didn't make up for it.

Granny was a great help at this time. As always, she seemed to understand how Gabrielle was feeling. She bought some special treats for their teas and talked to Gabrielle about Paris, saying that one day maybe Gabrielle would go there to swim in a championship.

The more time Gabrielle spent with her grandmother, the more she realized that she was a really special person and very wise. Sometimes when she came home she found Granny reading her Bible or praying. One day she asked her about it.

'Why do you read the Bible?' she said. 'Isn't it a very hard book to understand? Wouldn't you rather read some exciting story books?'

'Well, Gabby,' answered Granny, 'the Bible isn't a boring old book, even though it was written thousands of years ago. Actually, it's a library of sixty-six books, and there are some incredibly exciting stories in it!'

'Can you tell me some of them?' asked Gabrielle.

Granny smiled. 'There's nothing I'd like to do more!' she answered. 'How about we have a story at bedtime each evening?'

So they began a new routine, and, every evening before bed, Granny told Gabrielle some of the wonderful and fascinating Bible stories. Gabrielle recognized some of them—like Daniel in the lions' den, Noah building an ark, and especially the story of Joseph, because at school they had done a production of *Joseph and the Amazing Technicolor Dreamcoat*. She recognized the Christmas story too, although she hadn't realized it came from the Bible. Granny had a wonderful way of telling stories, and story-time became Gabby's favourite bit of the day.

She also asked Granny about praying: what it meant and why she did it.

She was surprised when Granny explained about how Jesus could be her friend, and that she could talk to him just as she talked to her dad and to her friend Paula, and could share everything with him. Gabrielle had no idea that God was real and so interested in her.

'I think you must be like God, Granny,' Gabrielle said to her. 'You're my very best friend and I can share everything with you—and you care so much about me.'

When Granny heard this, she turned away, not wanting Gabrielle to see the tears in her eyes. 'Darling, I love you very much, just as I do all my children and grandchildren. But one day I will die. Everybody dies one day. Your granddad has died already, and, because he loved God, he is now with God in heaven. I hope it won't happen for a long time yet, but I will get old and die. I hope that you will know God in that special way yourself so that you will never be alone, whatever happens to you in life.'

'I'd like to know Jesus as my friend,' Gabrielle replied. 'How do I do it?'

'All you need to do is ask God to come and live inside you, the real "you", the Gabby that thinks and feels. However, there is a barrier between us and God: something that separates us all from him and has to be dealt with first of all before we can know him as our friend.'

'What's that?' asked Gabrielle.

'It's something the Bible calls "sin". These days, you don't often hear that word. People think it's old fashioned. It means all the wrong things we have said, done and thought during our lives. All of us have sinned. There's not one person walking on the earth who hasn't said, thought or done something wrong. God is perfect. We call him "holy". He can't have anything to do with sin. He hates sin, and cannot be friends with people who have sinned.'

'But you just said that God and Jesus can be my friend!' exclaimed Gabrielle. 'And now you're saying God can't be my friend because of sin!'

'There is a solution, but only one,' continued Granny. 'The Bible says that God loved us so much that he made a way for us to become his friends. He sent Jesus, his Son, who was totally perfect, to come and live on the earth. Not only did Jesus teach us about God, he also took the death penalty that we deserved for our sin, and he died on the cross. That is what it means when at Easter we talk about Jesus dying for our sins.

'Because Jesus has already taken the punishment for us, if we are truly sorry for all the sin in our lives and we tell him so and ask for his forgiveness, then he does forgive us, and we can become children of God and friends of Jesus.

'If you really want to know God and become his child, you will need to tell him how sorry you are for the wrong things you have done, thought and said, and he will forgive you, because Jesus took the punishment in your place when he died on the cross.'

'Like when I ran away to Paula's party?' asked Gabrielle. 'I still feel bad inside when I think about that!'

'Yes, and all the times when you've said things which were unkind or untrue, or thought bad thoughts, or not done something you know you should have done. We all do so many wrong things every day. I need to say sorry to God every day.'

'You do?' Gabrielle gasped in surprise. 'But you're wonderful, Granny, and you don't do naughty things!'

'Yes, I do. Like everyone else, I think, say and do wrong things. The important thing is to say sorry to the person you have hurt and also to God our Father.'

Although Gabrielle didn't understand all this very well, she knew deep down inside that she felt bad about some of the naughty things she had done; they made her feel ashamed. She knew how selfish she was and how she really expected everyone to run around her because she was a gifted swimmer. Sometimes she lied to get her own way. It all made her feel really bad. Maybe she was too bad for God to forgive her. She wanted to be like Granny, good and loving, and she also wanted to be sure that one day she would go to heaven like Granny. She needed to think about these things a bit more.

Over the next few days Gabrielle kept thinking about God and Jesus. To think that God had loved her so much that he had sent Jesus to take her punishment! That amazed her. She felt worse and worse about the lies she told so easily to get out of trouble, the times she had been deceitful, how often she had been unkind to Amy, rude to her parents, and just so selfish about her swimming. The more she thought about it all, the more awful she felt. Some days she tried to forget it and just get on with her life, but the feeling of being so bad just wouldn't go away. Gabrielle thought about what Granny had said. She did feel sorry about the 'sin' in her life, and she did want to get rid of it.

One evening it all came to a head. Granny had been telling her about Jesus being the way, the truth and the life. Gabrielle thought she understood. She certainly wanted Jesus to forgive her.

'Do you think I'm too bad for God to forgive me?' she asked. Tears began to roll down her face. 'I really have done some horrible things, Granny, and I can't get them out of my head.'

'Whatever we have done, if we say sorry to God, he promises to forgive us and make us clean and new.'

'Please help me to pray and ask God to forgive my sins and come into my life,' Gabrielle said.

Granny took Gabrielle's hands in hers and said, 'Gabby, I want you to think very hard about this. You will be making a commitment to God that will last for ever. It may be hard sometimes because people do not understand and will make fun of you. It's like when you made up your mind to be a swimmer. Following Jesus means sacrifices and being different, but it's so worthwhile. I have never regretted my decision to be a Christian, but it hasn't always been easy.'

Gabrielle nodded. 'I understand, Granny. Sometimes my friends think I'm crazy to get up every morning and train. They tell me to "get a life!" But I just tell them that swimming is what I want to do.'

Once she was sure that Gabrielle did understand, Granny said a simple prayer which Gabrielle repeated after her, asking God to forgive her sins, come into her life and be her friend for ever.

Gabrielle knew that God had heard her. The old nagging feeling of being bad, which had bothered her especially since Paula's party, immediately disappeared. Inside she knew that something had changed, although she couldn't have explained it. She looked at Granny with shining eyes and said, 'Thank you!'

Chapter six

The end of the summer term came at last. Amy,
Gabrielle and Paul were all looking forward to the
long summer holidays. The weather had been warm and
sunny so far through July and they hoped it would continue
and that they would be able to play outside in the garden
and go to the park. For two weeks in August the family had
booked a caravan by the seaside. This time Granny Price
wasn't coming with them; she was going away on a holiday
with some of her friends. Gabrielle knew that she was
going to miss her very much, as Granny had become such
a special friend through the last year and done so much to
help her. She was glad, though, that Granny would have a
lovely holiday.

Gabrielle was excited as she packed her suitcase with
lots of jeans, shorts and T-shirts. She thought how nice it
would be not to have to wake up so early every morning
and go to training!

It was soon time to go away, so, very early one Saturday
morning, they set off for Weymouth. The car was so
jammed full of cases and bags that the three children were
quite squashed in the back seat, but they didn't mind. Once

they were on the road, they dozed off, even though they were so excited. They stopped half-way at a service station. By that time they were all starving, so Dad allowed them to have a cooked breakfast before they went back on the road. This was a great treat, and Gabrielle wondered if the whole holiday would be full of treats. She hoped so!

Before lunch-time they had arrived at the caravan site. It was huge! There were rows and rows of caravans, a couple of shops and a swimming pool on the site. 'I thought Gabby might just like to have a swim sometimes!' laughed Dad. 'She might even want to get up early in the morning!'

'No way!' replied Gabrielle. 'I'm going to lie in every day!'

The caravan was large—more like a house on wheels. The children chose their bunks and began to unpack their clothes while Mum sorted out some lunch. As soon as they had eaten the family went to explore the way to the beach. They couldn't wait to have fun in the sea!

The weather continued to be fine and sunny, and the holiday was just perfect. They spent a lot of time on the beach, swimming, playing in an inflatable boat that Mum and Dad had bought them, digging holes in the sand, and eating ice-creams. All the children made friends with other children staying on the site. Everyone seemed so friendly. Amy made friends with Saffron, an Asian girl who lived in Leicester with her parents. She was an only child and the same age as Amy. By the end of the first week of the holiday, the two were inseparable, and often Mum would ask Saffron to have tea with them.

The holiday was going by so quickly and there were just a few days left when something dreadful happened.

Saffron's family had decided to join the Price family and drive around the coast to a small cove, where it was rocky and the children could take their nets and fish in the rock pools. It was not quite as hot and sunny as it had been, but it was still nice enough for them to enjoy sitting on the rocks and having a picnic. Gabrielle, Amy and Paul were interested in the very different kinds of food that Saffron's family had brought. Their food was spicy and very tasty. After lunch the children were told that they could not swim just yet, but they could go off and explore the rock pools, as long as they were careful. Paul said that he just wanted to lie down and read his latest mystery book, so the girls went off together. They had their nets and buckets with them and skipped from pool to pool, delighted at finding lots of shrimps, crabs and other sea life. They didn't realize how far out they were going, and they were soon out of sight of the grown-ups.

Then Saffron wanted to go further round to the next cove.

'I don't think we should go any further,' said Gabrielle. 'Let's stop here—there are lots of pools here.'

'Don't be a spoil-sport!' said Amy. 'Saffron wants to go round just one more corner, that's all.'

Gabrielle wasn't sure about this, but the younger girls had run on ahead, so she thought she had better follow them. She glanced up at the sky, which was getting a bit dark, and noticed that the tide was coming in with waves which were growing larger. Amy and Saffron were shrieking with delight as they filled their buckets with treasures, but they were going further and further away.

Suddenly, a large wave swept Saffron off the rock where

she was fishing and into the sea. Amy screamed and tried to grab her, but she was almost swept away by the strong tide too.

In a flash, Gabrielle dropped her bucket and net and ran as near as she could to Saffron, who kept bobbing under the water. Without even thinking about it, Gabrielle shouted at Amy to go and get their dad, then she dived into the sea and swam towards Saffron. Even though she was such a good swimmer, Gabrielle found that swimming in the rough sea was very difficult. She eventually managed to reach Saffron and hold her head above the water, just as she had seen the children in the life-saving class do. She began to swim on her back and try to get to the shore, but the current was very strong and it was extremely difficult. Gabrielle then felt a rock against her back, and her right leg became incredibly painful, then useless. With her one good leg, she struggled on until she reached the shore, and then she passed out.

Chapter seven

Gabrielle woke up to see flashing lights and people everywhere, and there was a lot of noise. She wondered what was going on and tried to get up, but, as she moved, pain shot through her whole body. She realized that there was a mask on her face and she tried to pull it off. Where was she? What had happened? Her head ached and she couldn't remember anything.

'Mum,' she called out, and was so glad to hear Mum's voice answer, 'I'm right here, Gabby, lie still. The helicopter is coming to take you to hospital.'

'Hospital?' whispered Gabrielle. 'What's wrong?'

'Don't you remember? You jumped into the sea to rescue Saffron, and you were injured,' answered Mum.

'Oh,' replied Gabrielle, struggling to remember.

'Just try to lie still, darling,' she heard Dad's voice say.

'Paul, Amy and Saffron—where are they?' Gabrielle asked.

'They're all fine. Paul and Amy are with Saffron's mum. Saffron is fine now, but she's just being checked over by the doctor to make sure that she won't suffer any after-effects. You saved her life, darling, and we're so proud! Now you must be brave as you go to the hospital for treatment, as you've been injured on the rocks.'

Gradually it came back to her: the struggle to swim against the tide, the pain, and then the blackness that had swamped her.

The noise above her was tremendous and the wind swirled around as the helicopter landed on the cliff above them. Soon the paramedics had her carefully balanced as they carried the stretcher up the narrow path to the cliff-top. Mum was one side and Dad the other. She had been given an injection and it had numbed her pain but made her very sleepy.

'We'll soon have you in Dorchester, young lady,' the pilot said to her.

Carefully she was lifted into the helicopter, and the next thing Gabrielle knew was when she woke up in a hospital bed.

She looked around and saw the crisp white sheets and a tube running into her arm, Mum sitting one side of the bed and Dad the other. It all came flooding back to her again. Gabrielle tried to sit up, but the pain in her back and leg stopped her. She felt frightened, and tears began to run down her cheeks.

'It's all right, Gabby, don't cry,' said Mum. 'You've been badly injured, but the doctors have operated and in time the pain will go and you will be better.'

Gabrielle could see that Mum was trying not to cry.

'Oh, my little Tigger!' said Dad. 'You've been so brave and are such a hero! We're all so proud of you; if you hadn't dived in to rescue Saffron, she would have drowned. You saved her just in time! Now you must get lots of rest and mend all your broken bones.'

Broken bones! With horror, Gabrielle realized what that would mean. She would get behind in her swimming training and maybe not be selected for the British squad!

'But, Dad,' she was sobbing now, 'what about my swimming?'

'It'll wait until you're well—you mustn't worry about that now,' he replied.

Mum stayed at the hospital with her and Dad left to pick up and take care of Amy and Paul. They were with Saffron's father, because Saffron had also been kept in the hospital for a night to make sure she was all right after nearly drowning. Her mum was staying with her, but they were in the children's ward, whereas Gabrielle was in the intensive care ward.

The next day, because she was feeling a lot better, Gabrielle was wheeled down to the children's ward too. When she arrived, she saw that Saffron was getting dressed and packing her things to go home. Saffron and her mum came over to her and began to cry.

'I don't know how to say thank you to you, Gabrielle,' Saffron's mum said. 'If it wasn't for you, our only daughter would be dead! You were so very brave!'

Saffron was also crying. 'I'm so sorry,' she sobbed. 'You said to come back, and I didn't listen.'

For a few minutes Gabrielle didn't know what to say. She hated seeing people cry, especially grown-ups.

'It's OK,' she said, a bit awkwardly, 'but I think you'd better pray for me like my Granny does, so that I can quickly get better and swim again!'

'I've been praying almost all night,' said Mum. 'I also phoned Granny to ask her to pray.'

'We'll never forget you,' said Saffron's mum, 'and, although we have to go home tomorrow, we'll come and visit you very soon.'

Gabrielle turned and looked at Mum. 'What about us? We should be going home too. Dad has to go back to work. Are you going to leave me here all alone?' she asked, with a sense of panic rising and making her feel sick.

'Whatever we do, we will NOT leave you here alone!' replied Mum. 'Later today, when Dad comes in, we'll talk to the doctor and know a little more, but don't worry: one of us will stay with you if that's needed. Amy and Paul are coming with Dad and can't wait to see you, so have a sleep now so that you'll be fresh to chat to them.'

So Gabrielle said goodbye to Saffron and Saffron's mum, and tried to settle down to sleep. It was hard: she had to stay on her back because of the tube running into her arm and the plaster on her legs, but eventually she drifted into sleep.

Amy and Paul came to see Gabrielle that afternoon, and their parents left them to chat together while they went to talk to the doctor in charge of Gabrielle.

The three children were really quiet, not quite knowing what to talk about. Then Paul shyly began to tell his sister how very proud he was because she had been so brave.

Amy began to cry a little as she told Gabrielle that she thought that Saffron had died and that, when the helicopter came, Gabrielle herself might die too.

'I prayed and asked God to help you,' whispered Amy.

'So did I,' said Paul. 'I know he heard me because you're going to be fine!'

Gabrielle had wanted to tell them before about her

decision to ask Jesus to be her Saviour, and now she had the opportunity.

'You know,' she said, 'while I've been staying at Granny's through the weekdays, I've been learning so much about Jesus and God, and I've become a Christian! I've been learning to talk to Jesus about everything, and I know that he does hear.'

Suddenly the ward doors flew open and there was a bustle as the ward sister came in followed by a couple of men with cameras and lights.

'Well now, Gabrielle,' Sister said, 'you're famous! These men have come to interview you for Spotlight South-West television! They want to hear your story. Now, young men,' Sister turned to the reporters, 'only ten minutes, and don't make Gabrielle tired—she's been through a lot!'

The reporter asked some questions and Gabrielle tried to answer as best she could, just telling them what had happened. Then he asked about her swimming: was it true that she was in the trials for the British junior squad?

Paul could see that Gabrielle was struggling not to cry when he talked about the trials, so he answered for her, and also told them how very proud he was of his young sister.

True to her word, Sister was back in ten minutes, shooing the men away. All the other children on the ward who were well enough were shouting over the beds asking questions. Gabrielle was glad that Paul was there to help her out. The more she thought about the swimming, the more she realized that it might be a very long time before her leg and back healed, and she would be left far behind in her training. A tear began to trickle down her face because the thought crossed her mind that she might not get to the Olympics; she might never realize her ambition of winning a gold medal.

When Mum and Dad came back into the ward, they saw a rather subdued trio of children. Amy told them about the television crew and the interview.

Dad asked Mum to take Paul and Amy to the café to get a drink, and he sat with Gabrielle and held her hand.

'We've talked to the doctor,' he told her, 'and he has said that he will try to get a bed for you in our own hospital early next week. By then he thinks you will be comfortable enough to travel by ambulance. You will have to stay in hospital for at least a couple of weeks, but Mum, Granny or I will always be with you. I'm going to drive home tomorrow with Amy and Paul, and Granny will look after them while I'm at work, and Mum will stay here with you.

'It's going to be painful for you for a while, and it's too early to say how long it will be before you're back to normal. It's hard to be patient, but will you try?'

'Yes, Dad,' Gabrielle promised. 'But I'm not very good at keeping still!'

'We know that,' Dad replied, 'but it is important that you do what the doctors and nurses tell you. And remember: we all love you very much!'

Gabrielle snuggled down under the sheet and closed her eyes. She was very, very tired.

Early the next day, Dad drove Paul and Amy home and Mum stayed at the hospital with Gabrielle. She was sad not to be going back home with them and especially wished she could see Granny Price. She knew she had to be still and let her bones heal, so she began to pray and ask God to help her. It was so hard to have to stay in bed! Yet, when she did move, it hurt so much!

As she lay in bed, Mum told her stories of what it was like when she was a little girl, and she read books to her. Some of the time Gabrielle slept, especially after the nurses had given her the pain-killing medicine.

During the afternoon, some visitors arrived. Saffron had come with her parents to say goodbye before they started their journey home. They had bought a present for Gabrielle: an iPod loaded with music that she could listen to as she lay in bed. Saffron and her parents promised to keep in touch. How could they ever forget the brave girl who had saved their daughter's life?

On Monday morning the doctors and nurses came to Gabrielle's bed and discussed her progress. They felt that she was fit enough to travel in an ambulance to the hospital near her home. The ward sister had been making arrangements and was pleased to tell them that Queen Mary's Hospital for Children had room for her, and they hoped to move her the next day. That was good news! Gabrielle tried very hard to keep still and quiet all day so that she would be able to manage the journey.

The journey seemed very long. Even though she had been given strong pain-killers, she found it very uncomfortable to lie still. She tried to listen to her music and then to sleep, but nothing seemed to help her pain. Gabrielle was so glad when at last they arrived at Carshalton and she was gently helped into a bed on the ward. Once she was settled she found herself drifting off to sleep.

When she woke up she felt as if she had slept for days! She also felt so much better, and, as she looked around, she was delighted to see that Granny was sitting beside her.

'Oh, Granny!' said Gabrielle, and suddenly tears began to pour out of her eyes and down her face. 'Oh, Granny, I don't think I'll be able to swim for a long time!'

Granny found a tissue and wiped her eyes. 'Don't worry about that now,' she said. 'All you have to worry about is getting better. Mum has gone home to rest, so I'll stay with you. I am so proud of you, Gabby—what you did was very brave!

'I've been praying for you and I believe that somehow God will work it all out. He promises that all the things that happen to us he will work out in some way for our good, if we trust him.'

'I've been praying too, Granny, and so has Paul. I told him and Amy about becoming a Christian.'

'That's wonderful!' Granny answered. 'And we will all keep praying because these next few weeks won't be easy.'

And they certainly were not easy. There were some good days, including the days when the drip was taken out of Gabrielle's arm and when the nurses started to help her get up and dressed. There were also bad days, when the pain just would not go away, and when Gabrielle realized that she could not walk until the plaster was changed.

One week seemed to drift into another, and the days were long and boring. Her teacher sent her some school-work once the new term started, but Gabrielle was getting worried as it was time to visit senior schools and for the swimming coaching to begin again. She was sure she would be in the second division even if she was able to start swimming again very soon. She thought of all she had sacrificed to train for the national team, and all that her family had given up so that she could do it, and it didn't seem fair. She felt very cross with God. She was glad she had saved Saffron's life, but why did she have to get injured? Sometimes she was so angry with God that she didn't want to talk to him any more. Was he really a Father who cared?

As the days went by Gabrielle became more and more grumpy. Sometimes she snapped at Mum or Granny, who spent a lot of time with her. Then she felt mean because she knew how kind they were, and it wasn't their fault that she had been badly injured.

Sadly the doctors discovered that her injuries were worse than they had first thought. Her spine had been damaged and one leg smashed so badly that it hung a bit limp and useless from her body. Each morning the physiotherapist strapped her into a canvas corset to support her and helped her into a wheelchair. She had learnt to use her arms well and manoeuvre the chair around the ward at quite a speed, but when she tried to stand up in the gym and walk holding two bars, it was agony.

One day her anger boiled over.

'I hate God!' she announced to Mum and Granny as they sat in the ward with her. 'Why did he do this to me?' she asked.

For a while Granny was quiet and Mum had tears rolling down her face.

'God didn't do that to you, Gabby,' Granny explained. 'Bad things happen in this world. God doesn't say that bad things won't happen to his children, but he does promise to help us through whatever comes.'

'Even this?' Gabrielle now began to cry bitterly. 'I want to walk again and I want to swim again!'

'Well, let's ask him together, shall we?' Granny suggested.

Gabrielle nodded, and so did Mum. Granny then asked God very simply to help Gabrielle to walk and to swim again, and also to be able to be happy and cope with each day that came along.

It wasn't long after this that the physiotherapist asked Mum to bring in Gabrielle's swimming costume. She was going to start hydrotherapy in the hospital pool.

At first Gabrielle was frightened to get back into the water, and she didn't even want to try to swim, but then she found that she was able to move more easily when she was in the pool, and the wonderful feeling of being in the water again thrilled her. Before long she was swimming and loving it! She was not as fast as before the accident, but it made her feel so good! It helped her leg, too, and as the muscles grew stronger, so she began to walk a little. A splint was made to fit and support her leg, and that helped her, along with a special boot to make her legs the same length. Gabrielle's excitement at being able to swim again had made her much happier. She realized that God was answering Granny's prayer, and she too started to pray again as well.

The doctors and nurses, physiotherapists and occupational therapists had all been working together and making plans for Gabrielle to go home. Gabrielle knew that things would be different, but how she longed to get home again!

Chapter eight

Everyone was very excited when the doctors told Gabrielle that she could finally go home. Her mother planned a surprise party for her, putting 'Welcome Home!' banners on the gate and door, and lots of balloons all around the house. Dad had taken a day off work and helped her walk from the car into their home. When she came in, there was a great shout of 'Surprise!' as many of her friends had come to welcome her. Then two small brown arms were suddenly around her neck, and she realized it was Saffron! Saffron and her family had come all the way from Leicester! Amy was beside herself with happiness because not only had her sister come home, but also her best friend had come to stay! Paula was also waiting for her. She had often visited Gabrielle in the hospital, and she always told her all the news from school.

Soon Gabby was sitting on the sofa and talking to everyone. It was so good to be home! Mum and Granny Price were in the kitchen, getting a wonderful party tea ready, when the doorbell rang. Paul went to answer it and ran back into the room very excited!

'You'll never guess who has come!' he said. 'It's Jane and John from the canal-boat!'

In his excitement he had left them standing at the door, but they understood completely. The family were so pleased to see them again.

'It's so kind of you all to come and welcome me home!' said Gabrielle. 'I didn't know I had so many friends. Thank you so much!'

They had a great tea party, and at the end Granny came in with a cake. It was like a birthday cake, but written on it in red icing were the words 'To the bravest girl in the world!'

Everyone cheered as Gabrielle cut it. She felt very special, and thought to herself that it must feel like a bit like this to be on the podium at the Olympics when you have won a medal. To think such thoughts didn't make her cry any more because secretly she had decided that one day, even if it took a very long time, she would still win that gold medal!

When everyone had gone home Gabrielle felt very tired. Mum helped her undress and get into the bed which they had made for her in the lounge. Her physiotherapist had warned her that it might be some weeks before she would be able to use her bedroom upstairs. She had also promised to send another physiotherapist to work with her at home, and that Gabrielle would still go twice a week by ambulance to the hydrotherapy pool. She had been told that it might be a long time before she could go back to school. 'We'll see about that!' Gabrielle thought to herself. She had decided she would work as hard at her exercises as she did at her swimming training, and she would get to school soon!

There was one problem, however. Which senior school would she go to next year? Paula had told her about the visits she had made and which school she had put down as her first choice. Gabrielle wanted to go to the same one as her best friend, but not all schools were suitable for someone who had problems with walking. Gabrielle knew now that she might have to use a wheelchair for some time. It was something that worried her. Her school had sent work into the hospital so she had been able more or less to keep up with her class, and her teacher promised to do the same now that she was at home, and even to come and visit her, but Gabrielle was still worried about the future.

One day she told Granny about her worries. Granny, as always, suggested that they talk to God about the problem, so they did. About a week later a teacher came to visit. Gabrielle didn't know this teacher as she was new to the school, but Paula had told her how nice she was. She was full of fun and laughter, and told Gabrielle that she was pleased with the work she was doing at home, and that the school was so proud of her and had nominated her for an award for bravery. She also asked about senior school. Had the Prices filled in their form yet to indicate which school was their first choice for Gabrielle?

When she found that they hadn't yet done this, she talked with Mum about different options, suggesting a school which would mean a little more travelling but which was adapted for wheelchairs and pupils who had problems with walking. It also had a lovely heated swimming pool, where Gabrielle could continue to swim.

'I've heard all about our future Olympic champion!' the teacher said. 'You mustn't give up on your dreams!'

'I love to swim,' answered Gabrielle, 'but my spine and leg have been so badly damaged, it'll take me years to catch up!'

'Well, there are always the Paralympics,' was her reply. 'I have a brother who's blind, and he's training for the Paralympics in athletics. It takes more skill and determination than for able-bodied competitors. To win a medal in those games means even more than in the "normal" Olympics.'

'Does it really?' asked Gabrielle, a glint coming into her eyes at the thought. 'I wonder … do you think it might be possible for me to be a good swimmer again?'

'Absolutely!' replied her teacher. 'If you really want to do it, I suggest you try for St Anne's School. You'll get so much help and encouragement there!'

When Granny came to see her the next day, Gabrielle's mind was made up. She told her that she was determined to try to swim well again and enter the Paralympics. She told her, too, about her teacher's suggestion of going to St Anne's School, as she would get help and support there.

'What a great answer to our prayers!' said Granny. 'Here's a verse from the Bible for you to remember: Jeremiah 29 verse 11. It tells us that God knows the plans that he has for us, to prosper us and not to harm us, and to give us a hope and a future. Try to learn that verse by heart, because it will encourage you.'

Gabrielle asked Granny to get her Bible from the shelf and together they found the verse. Gabrielle marked it in red. She thought she would learn it by heart that very evening.

Gabrielle's parents filled in the school form asking for

St Anne's School to be first choice, and explaining their daughter's special needs and their reason for choosing that school. Mrs Castle, the new teacher, also wrote a letter to the Education Authority, telling them about her pupil.

Gabrielle had to miss a whole term at school, but she worked very hard with the physiotherapist to strengthen her leg and back muscles. She also loved her times in the pool and was beginning to swim well again, in spite of her bad leg. She made her arms work twice as hard! She even worked very hard at her lessons at home. Paul was often helpful as he explained things she found hard.

Just before Christmas she was able to begin to go upstairs and sleep in her bedroom with Amy again. She had to have the bottom bunk while Amy had the top one, but she didn't mind too much; it was just so good to be more normal again! She and Amy were really good friends now. In fact, the accident had brought all three children very much closer together. Paul and Amy often played board games with Gabrielle in the evenings, or they would watch a DVD together.

Christmas was great fun. Somehow it was extra-special because, after all that had happened, Gabrielle now appreciated her home and family in a new way. She also understood in a new way that Christmas was a celebration of Jesus's birthday. Since the accident, Mum and Dad had started to go to church with Granny Price and to take the children. Much to their surprise, they all enjoyed going and were making lots of new friends. On Christmas Eve, Gabrielle's parents decided that they would take the family to the midnight service. They were all excited about going out so late and they wrapped up very warmly as it was a cold night. Dad wheeled Gabrielle in her wheelchair down to the church. It was magical! The church was decorated and the Christmas tree was huge and covered in lots of twinkling lights! The children gasped as they went in. They sang the carols with great gusto, and somehow Gabrielle felt that God was very near to her. She knew that he would make everything all right.

After Christmas, when the new term started, Gabby felt quite shy about returning to school in a wheelchair. Although she could walk short distances with help, she needed a chair most of the time. It made her feel different from everybody else, and she hated that! They set off early for school on the first day of term, and Gabrielle was so pleased to see Paula waiting for her at the school gates. As her classmates began to arrive, they all came over to talk to her, and soon Gabrielle forgot that she was in a wheelchair. They all started to tell one another about the Christmas holidays and all the fun they had had. When the bell rang, Gabrielle wheeled herself up to the door, even though Paula wanted to push her.

'No, I must do it myself and make my arm muscles strong,' she explained. 'I need to be independent as much as possible! If I let everyone push me all the time, the physiotherapist says I'll quickly get weak.'

It wasn't easy getting into the classroom, but, once in, she got out of the chair and managed to reach her desk. It seemed strange to be back in class after so many weeks of being in hospital or at home and trying to study alone. She was very relieved that she seemed to understand what was going on in all the lessons, even the maths. She was glad that Paul had helped her at home.

Her new teacher was very kind and, when it was assembly, she asked the whole school to give Gabrielle a clap to welcome her back. Then the headmistress read out a letter to the school which told them that the nomination they had sent in for a bravery award had been considered and Gabrielle Price had been awarded a 'Children of Courage' award! Everyone gasped! Then they clapped and cheered. Gabrielle felt herself going pink, and tears were quickly collecting in her eyes. She didn't know what to say.

'We are so proud of Gabrielle Price,' said the headmistress. 'She won many trophies for the school with her swimming. We thought that that was wonderful, and were proud of the way she undertook her training programme with such commitment. But what she did when she risked her own life in order to save a little girl from drowning has been a far, far greater achievement. This school will always be proud of her, and she truly deserves this award. We are pleased to tell her that she has been invited to attend a special ceremony, and Prince Harry will present her with the award!'

What a start to the New Year! It was all very exciting. About two weeks later Mum took her to London in order to buy a really nice dress. Normally Gabrielle liked to wear jeans, but she realized that this was a very important occasion and so she needed a 'posh' dress. They found a lovely deep-red velvet dress, and then they bought some shiny black patent leather shoes. Most of the time Gabrielle had to wear a boot which was built up on her bad leg, but for this special occasion she could do without it!

When the day of the award ceremony came, Mum and Dad accompanied her to London. Gabrielle was just a little sad that Amy, Paul and Granny weren't allowed to come too; there were only tickets for two people to accompany each child.

Dad took his video camera so that he would be able to make a film of the event. That way, the others would be able to share the great day. They went to a very exclusive hotel and joined a group of other children who were all dressed in their best and waiting excitedly with their parents. Some of them looked very sick and, even though she still needed the wheelchair most of the time, Gabrielle felt that many of the children were far worse off than she was.

There was a very kind lady who welcomed them and gave Gabrielle a badge with her name on it. The lady led the three of them to a table, which had a lace cloth and a lovely red rose in a silver vase. It was quite near the stage at the front of the room, so Gabrielle was very excited; she would have a good view of all that went on.

When it was time to start and everybody was seated, Prince Harry arrived. All those who were able to do so stood up and clapped. Then the Master of Ceremonies gave a speech, welcoming everyone and saying what an honour it was to meet these courageous children. Each child was called up in turn, in alphabetical order, and the audience was told about their bravery. Some children had overcome great problems in their lives, some had been very brave through terrible illness, some had been carers for their sick parents or brothers and sisters, and some, like Gabrielle, had helped others, even at the risk of their own lives. When Gabrielle's name was called, she got out of her wheelchair and managed, with her mother's help, to walk slowly to the front. The story was told of her rescue of Saffron, and everyone clapped and cheered. The Prince shook her by the hand.

'You are a very brave girl, Gabrielle,' he said. 'I hope you soon recover from your injury. I understand that you were training for the junior Olympic swimming squad.'

'Yes, Your Highness, I was,' she whispered, overwhelmed that Prince Harry was talking to her.

'Keep on having courage and don't give up on your dreams,' replied the Prince.

'Yes, sir. I hope to enter the Paralympics if I'm not fit enough for the Olympic team.'

'Britain will be proud of you, even as we are proud of you tonight,' Prince Harry replied, as he gave her a certificate and an envelope.

Gabrielle went pink with delight and almost fell as she tried to walk off the stage in her shiny black shoes! Fortunately the Master of Ceremonies and Mum were there with helping hands!

When the ceremony was over, they were all given a wonderful meal before they set off for home.

'I shall never forget this evening,' said Gabrielle.

'Nor will we!' replied her parents in unison.

Gabrielle unrolled her certificate. 'I shall get that framed and hang it on the wall!' Dad said.

Then she opened the envelope. Inside was a cheque for more money than she had ever owned in her life: £100! Gabrielle gasped in surprise.

'What shall I do with this?' she asked Mum.

'I think for now it would be best to put it in the bank until you've had time to think!' Mum replied.

Chapter nine

After all the excitement of the award ceremony, life settled down into a routine. Every day Gabrielle worked really hard, both at school and with her exercises to strengthen her leg and back. The pain was much weaker than it used to be, so gradually she was able to use the wheelchair a bit less and walk more. She dragged her 'bad' leg behind her and sometimes tripped over it, but she was determined to improve her walking and one day not need the chair at all. All the discipline of her swimming training before the accident was helping her now to be determined and brave.

When February half-term came, Dad had a surprise for them all.

'I've booked the cottage again at Limpley Stoke so that we can all have a week of fun together. Our friends John and Jane on the canal-boat will be moored near the village, and we hope to be able to spend some time with them. Also, we can take Gabrielle to see the places she missed last year because of the training sessions!'

Everyone cheered.

'I hope Granny Price is coming too,' said Gabby.

'Of course!' answered Mum. 'She loved it when we were there before, and it was she who made friends with John and Jane!'

So once again the family packed up their bags and set off. It was so exciting to be going back to the cottage they had loved so much! Even though it was only February, the sun shone and it seemed quite warm. Gabrielle enjoyed seeing some of the sights of Bath, but most of all she loved it when they visited John and Jane on the boat. She found herself telling them about her time in hospital and how she had been angry with God, but then had begun to pray again, and how God had answered her prayers. She told them how determined she was to win a gold medal for her country one day. She was not going to give up on her dream!

One day, Gabrielle was surprised because Dad suggested that they drive her up to the university campus at Claverton Down.

'Why are we going there?' she asked.

'Wait and see!' was Dad's reply.

They drove around the campus to the swimming pool. There waiting for them was Mr Black, her coach from before the accident, along with some of the students with whom she had trained the previous summer half-term.

'Surprise!' they shouted as she and Dad arrived at the pool. 'Here comes our young hero!'

There by the pool they had tied balloons and provided food for a party! Also there was a parcel for her.

'It's not my birthday!' she exclaimed.

'It's because we're so proud of you!' said Mr Black.

Gabrielle opened the parcel and inside found a complete

new set of swimming gear: costume, cap, goggles, and even a towel with the university crest!

'It's to encourage you to start to train again,' said one of the students. 'You have talent; don't let the injury stop you!'

'I won't,' said Gabrielle, with shining eyes. 'I've already decided to train again and try for the Paralympics. I've been told that I have a permanent injury to my leg and back, so will never be able to be in the mainstream Olympic team, but my teacher at school said that it takes more guts to win a medal in the Paralympics, so I'm determined to do it!'

'Great!' another of the students answered. 'Come on, go and change, and we'll swim together again and start you on the route to winning that gold! Afterwards we can eat all these goodies!'

So Gabrielle went to the changing-room and was soon in her new costume. It fitted perfectly! She put on the cap and goggles and went to the pool. She dived into the water. How good it felt to swim in the Olympic pool again! She knew she was far from fast, but she tried her best and really enjoyed the swimming work-out. Mr Black looked at her with admiration.

'I have no doubt that you will one day realize your dream and win that medal!' he said. 'I'm willing to take you on again and train you, even though you won't be able to be in the usual club. I'll talk to your parents when I get back home and we'll arrange something together.'

'Oh, thanks so much!' Gabrielle looked at Mr Black with her eyes shining. 'And thank you, too, for this wonderful surprise! It has made me feel so positive again! Thank you everybody!' She looked at the students who had befriended her last year. 'I shall never forget today!'

'Come on, I'm starving!' said the student who had planned the surprise. 'Let's eat!'

No one needed a second invitation! They all enjoyed the feast. There was a special cake, and Gabrielle was so pleased when she saw there was enough left for her to take back to the cottage for the rest of the family to share.

When she and Dad left the university she felt so encouraged and happy, especially to know that Mr Black was willing to help her train again.

Chapter ten

Mr Black was as good as his word. Once they were back at home, he contacted her parents and they began to talk about when would be the best time for Gabrielle to start her training. Amy was now taking ballet classes and doing very well, so she also needed to be taken to her lessons. Once again, Granny Price came to the rescue as they tried to work out a plan. She promised to help whenever she could with transport for either of the girls. It was agreed that she would take Gabrielle to the pool after school for her coaching, while Mum was getting tea ready. Gabrielle was very happy when she heard about the arrangement, because she had missed her special times with her grandmother. They had become such good friends when she was staying in her house during the week. Gabrielle was determined to work as hard as she could in the pool. There were three and a half years left before the next Olympic Games, and she wanted to be in the British squad!

She started by training once a week, and it was exhausting. But quickly the training was increased to two days a week, and, as she became stronger, to three. Each time it caused her pain as she swam, but Gabrielle was determined to succeed, so she tried to ignore the pain. Mr Black hoped that in the summer term she might be able to manage four or even five sessions a week. He was always very encouraging and patient as he coached his pupil. He, too, believed that one day Gabrielle could be the star that she longed to be!

They had been back at school a couple of weeks after half-term when the all-important letter from the Education Authority arrived. Gabrielle squealed with delight when she heard that she had been given a place at St Anne's Senior School! She phoned Granny Price at once.

'God has answered our prayers,' she told Granny. 'I'm so happy!'

'That's wonderful news!' replied Granny. 'I'm delighted for you!'

'In the letter it also said that, because of my leg problems, the local authority will send a taxi to take me to school and back. Isn't that amazing! It will help so much as the school is a long way from home. Now I wonder which school Paula has got into. I can't wait to see her and find out!'

When she arrived at school that morning Paula was waiting for her.

'I got into Brides, the school I wanted! Did you get into St Anne's?' she asked Gabrielle.

'Yes,' answered her friend. 'And they're going to send a taxi to take me each day!'

'Wow! You must be special!' teased Paula. 'But I shall miss not being with you. We can still be best friends, though, and spend time together at the weekends.'

'You bet!' replied Gabrielle. 'I always want to do things with you! Maybe you'd like to come to our church with us on Sundays. I belong to a fab group called LiveWires.'

'Well, why not?' answered Paula. 'If it's OK with my mum and dad, then I'll come on Sunday.'

And so it was that Paula began to go to church with Gabrielle and her family. Gabrielle was so pleased to have her best friend with her. She began to tell Paula about her other friend, Jesus, and about how her prayers had been answered. It was lovely to be able to share the best secret of all—that of knowing and loving Jesus—with her best friend.

The Easter holidays came and went and soon they were in the summer term, their last term at primary school. Several outings had been arranged for the top class, and this time Gabrielle was able to go on them. Although she still needed her wheelchair, her class teacher was so helpful and made it easy for Gabrielle to join in. She was even able to go on the school journey to an adventure centre in the Quantock Hills in Somerset. They stayed in wooden log cabins from Monday until Friday. Gabrielle was in the cabin nearest the main building where everyone went for meals and talks. It was also near the showers, and with Paula's help she could manage to walk to them. There was a small outdoor swimming pool, and her friends were so impressed when they saw how strongly Gabrielle was able to swim again.

One night, they were woken up by a huge splash and a strange noise. The girls were a bit scared. They had no lights in the cabins, but had to scramble around to find their torches, wondering whatever was going on! The six

girls in Gabrielle's cabin decided to go and look outside
but staying close together, as they weren't sure what was
happening there. The noise was definitely strange: it was a
loud 'snorty' sort of noise, along with splashing.

They linked arms and went outside. It was very dark,
and at first they couldn't see very well. Eventually they
realized that there was a donkey in the pool! The poor
animal was thrashing around and obviously very scared.

'I'll run and knock on teacher's door,' said one of the
girls, and she began to run across to the main building.

'Don't try to rescue this donkey,' Paula said to Gabrielle,
'it's too big for you!'

'No way!' replied Gabrielle. 'But the poor thing must be
so frightened!'

The grown-ups were already awake, and the rest of the
class too. They all circled the pool with teeth chattering in
the cold.

'The fire brigade are on their way,' their teacher told
them. 'I suggest that we all go over to the main building
and have some hot chocolate while we wait for them.'

Although it was three o'clock in the morning, all the
children were wide awake by now and very excited. Hot
chocolate and biscuits were just what was needed, and
when the fire brigade arrived they all watched from the
window while two firemen waded into the pool and, along
with the local farmer whose donkey it was, and his sons,
carefully calmed the animal and helped it out of the water.

'Thank you, young people, for getting the fire brigade
so quickly,' the farmer said. 'This donkey is a very useful
animal, but sometimes he is very frisky and naughty! I
must take him home now and rub him down, but I'd like to

say thank you by inviting you all to come and see my farm tomorrow. Maybe you could come about 3 p.m. and see the milking. Then I'm sure that my wife will have some tea for you all!'

The class teacher said that they would love to come, and they said goodbye to the firemen and the farmer and his sons. Then the teacher packed the children off to bed, telling them that breakfast would be an hour later than normal so that they could lie in after all the night's excitement.

The visit to the farm was great fun. Not many of the class had been to a working farm before, as they lived in the town. In the yard was an old tractor, and the children were allowed to climb on it. As Gabrielle couldn't do that, the farmer took her to see a newborn calf.

'I was helping this young 'un to be born last night when the fire brigade rang!' he said. 'He's a fine young beast! There's his mum, in the corner. She'll feed him for a few days, and then I have to separate them. Sad, but it has to be done. We need the cow for her milk, and then the calf will go to market.'

Gabrielle felt sad that the lovely black and white calf would have to leave its mother so soon. She watched it go to its mother and nuzzle against her, drinking milk from her udders.

Just as the farmer had promised, the children were taken into the large farmhouse kitchen where a wonderful tea had been made for them. There were scones with jam and cream, all freshly baked, and lots of cakes! What a feast!

The farmer's wife laughed as she saw the children

tucking in. 'Nothing I like better than to see the young 'uns dig into the food I make!' she said. 'It does my heart good to see it, really it does!'

The time away with the school was such fun, and Gabrielle and Paula felt really sad that it was almost time to leave their primary school. Yet they both felt excited about their senior schools and all the new challenges they would face.

Term ended with the sports day and then a leavers' service. The sports day was always fun, but, this time, Gabrielle could not take part in very much. Her teacher made sure she was not left out and gave her several important jobs to do, like holding the tape and even using the starting gun. Even so, she did feel a bit sad at not being able to run as she used to. When Paula did the three-legged race with someone else, it reminded her of the previous summer and how they had fallen over and giggled so much! Gabrielle looked down at her bad leg and sighed. How she wished she could run! Then she told herself to stop being a misery, because she could still swim and she would one day swim well!

When it was the day for the leavers' service, the parents and friends were all invited. The top classes went with their teachers to the parish church, and when they arrived it seemed very full with all the visitors. Gabrielle looked round to see if she could see her parents and Granny, and she waved when she picked them out from the crowd. Also, to her surprise, she saw that Saffron's parents were sitting in the row with them. Gabrielle thought to herself, 'How kind of them to come such a long way!'

The service was very moving, and the children felt sad

in some ways. The vicar talked to them and encouraged them to enjoy senior school, but also to be good students. Then the headmistress announced that she had some school prizes to award, and some cups for sporting achievements. Paula was awarded the cup as netball captain, and Gabrielle was really pleased for her. Then she heard her name being called out.

'Gabrielle Price,' the headmistress said, 'you have been given a prize for the best overall improvement in all subjects over the year. It is very well deserved since you had to miss one whole term and you have struggled with pain and disability. Very well done!'

Everyone clapped very loudly, and a rather pink and embarrassed Gabrielle walked, with Paula's help, up to the front to receive her prize.

She shook the headmistress's hand and said thank you, and she was just turning to go and sit down again when the headmistress touched her arm and told her to wait.

'Just a minute, Gabrielle,' she said, 'you have a second award.'

Then the headmistress announced that some special guests had been invited to the leavers' service. She asked Mr and Mrs Patel, Saffron's parents, to come forward.

Mr Patel gave a little speech in which he told everybody how Gabrielle had saved his daughter's life because she was such a strong swimmer and also so selfless.

'We have come here today to present the swimming cup to Gabrielle, because in her years at this school she has won many cups and awards for the school and the county. She was due for selection for the British squad when the accident happened. The school has asked me today to present the swimming trophy to Gabrielle in acknowledgement that she is the best swimmer this school has ever had, and I am very proud to do that.'

Again, everyone clapped loudly as Gabrielle was given the silver cup.

'Thank you,' she said to Saffron's dad as she took it. 'I'll do my best to make everyone even more proud of me as I continue my swimming training at senior school.'

Chapter eleven

The school holidays had begun. Paul, Amy and Gabrielle looked forward to six weeks of just having fun and no homework to do! When the weather was fine they went together to the local park and played games with their friends. Although Gabrielle had to use her wheelchair and found it hard to walk easily, she found that she could still join in the fun. Paul was very protective of her. She was very good at hitting the ball if they were playing rounders or cricket, and he would run instead of her. That way she got to play and enjoy herself. Mum very often came in the afternoon with a picnic tea for them all. Some of the other mums did the same, and they sat and chatted as the children played. Wet days were more of a problem, but they liked to invent dressing-up games and make up their own plays to act. Paula often came round and joined in, as did friends of Paul and Amy too.

Amy was very excited when Saffron came to stay for a week. Saffron had Gabrielle's bed so that the girls could be together, and Gabrielle went down to Granny Price's house to sleep.

'It's like old times!' she said to Granny. 'I know I'm much

older now, but do you think we could have hot chocolate and Bible stories, just like we did when I lived with you?'

'Of course we can!' said Granny. 'We'll never be too old to do that!'

Gabrielle so enjoyed being back in her old room at Granny's. It was like having a special holiday of her own. Most days, after breakfast, she would go home and join in whatever the family were doing. She did ask, however, if she could stay with her granny for just one of the days.

The two of them had a great time together. They baked some cakes and then went shopping. Gabrielle felt very grown up when she helped Granny choose a new dress. They just enjoyed being together. She could tell Granny about all the things that worried her, especially about changing schools. They talked about the swimming training and her longing to win a gold medal. Granny Price always talked to her as if she was a grown-up, and it made her feel good. Then, when they got home and sat down, they were able to pray together about all her worries and hopes and dreams. It comforted Gabrielle a lot. Afterwards, they watched a Wallace and Gromit DVD together, and they laughed until they cried! It was a very happy day.

For the last two weeks of the summer holiday the family were going away together. This time it was not to a caravan; they were hiring a canal-boat and were going to join their friends John and Jane on the Kennet and Avon canal. The children were so excited! Granny was coming with them, but it had been arranged that she would stay with John and Jane on their boat, as there was not a lot of room on the one the family had hired. They had decided to travel by train to Bath and pick up the boat there. The canal started at Bath, and they had been told to pick up their boat on the banks of the river Avon at Widcombe; there they could join the canal and make their way up to meet their friends at Limpley Stoke.

Paul and Amy set to learn right away how to work the locks. It wasn't so easy for Gabrielle, but she was determined to try as well. At Deep Lock in Bath, the deepest canal lock in the country, Dad worked the lock gates himself. 'I'm not risking any of you falling into this lock!' he said. 'This is going to be a trouble-free holiday!'

Actually, Gabrielle liked staying inside the boat and feeling it rise up in the water. She wondered who had invented locks on the canal. How very clever that person must have been to make a sort of water staircase! Mum told her to wait until they reached the town of Devizes, for then they would have to go through twenty-nine locks—a real staircase!

Amy, Paul and Gabrielle took it in turns to help Dad steer, keeping the boat on the correct side of the canal and at the right speed.

'No more than four miles per hour!' said their dad. 'Any more will rock the boats around us as we pass, and that's very bad manners, like speeding on the roads!'

Their boat was a sixty-foot narrowboat, gaily painted in red and green and called *Cock Robin*. Inside, it was very compact; the two girls were soon exploring every nook and cranny.

'Look at the tiny loo and bath!' exclaimed Amy. 'And there's a shower, too!'

'I like the kitchen,' said Gabrielle. 'It's got everything, but all packed away so neatly.'

'It's not a kitchen,' remarked Paul, who was standing nearby. 'In a boat, it's called a galley.'

'OK, know-all! But I love it anyway!' replied his sister.

'If you love it so much, dear,' said Granny, who was sitting in an armchair, 'put the kettle on and make us all a cup of tea!'

'Great idea!' came Mum's voice. 'It'll be ages before we reach Limpley Stoke and meet up with Jane and John. Everything happens very slowly on the canal! There will be plenty of time for lots of cups of tea!'

Amy helped Gabrielle, and it was fun doing it together. There was no room for the wheelchair, so everyone helped Gabrielle to walk. When she had too much pain or was just too tired, her father carried her.

The children looked out through the little window and watched the mallard ducks swimming alongside them. Each time they passed another canal-boat, they waved, and the people waved back at them.

On the roof of the boat there were flower-pots, and it was like having a little garden on top of your house! Paul quickly found a book and decided that it was a special place for him to go and read whenever he could. Not that he had much peace, because very soon they came to a swing-bridge, and he and Amy had to learn how to unlock it and swing it to one side and then, once the boat had gone through, swing it back and lock it again.

By the time they reached the canal basin at Limpley Stoke, they had all had so much fun they didn't realize how long it had taken for them to do such a few miles! Dad steered the boat and moored up alongside the lock-keeper's cottage. Several other boats were already moored there.

Paul and Amy got off and quickly searched among the boats to find Jane and John's. They soon found their friends and they were all very pleased to see one another again. They brought Jane and John to *Cock Robin* so that they could collect Granny Price and her belongings. By that time, the kettle was on the boil again, ready for everyone to have another cup of tea.

That night, it was such fun getting ready for bed and sleeping on the narrow bunks. Paul had to sleep on a mattress in the 'living-room', but he didn't mind a bit. The girls were giggling and chatting about their trip for a long time, but finally they fell asleep.

The holiday was a great success. They travelled in tandem with Jane and John very slowly up the canal. Paul and Gabrielle learnt how to fish. They didn't catch very much, but it was fun trying. Sometimes they sat on the canal bank; at other times, when they were moored, they sat on the top of the boat. Every evening the two families ate together. If the weather was fine they liked to barbeque on the canal bank. In fact, the weather was fine almost every day. In the evenings after their meal they went for walks in the nearby woods. Gabrielle wasn't able to walk on the rough ground, so she either stayed on the boat with Granny and Jane or the men took it in turns to give her a piggyback. She was really too heavy for this, but they so much wanted her to be included in all the fun.

Amy had become very good at bird-spotting and she kept a diary of the birds she saw. It was Gabrielle, however, who had got up early one morning and was sitting in the bows of the boat and talking to God when she saw a kingfisher fly from a bush and catch a fish in the canal for its breakfast. The streak of blue was so beautiful that she gasped with amazement. She went to find her sister, but, by the time Amy appeared, the kingfisher had flown away.

The biggest challenge was to work the flight of twenty-nine locks at Devizes. It took all day! With two boats going up the flight together, there were plenty of people to help, especially since Jane and John lived and worked on the canal and were used to them. They were very relieved that it was a fine day! Granny said that she was very glad that she was an old lady and could just sit and watch!

At the end of the two weeks the children were sure that they had much bigger arm muscles because of working the locks! Gabrielle was pleased because, now that one of her legs was so much weaker, she needed really strong arm muscles to help her swim. Even though she had not been in training for two weeks she felt fit and strong. It would be good to get back to swimming again, and she was looking forward to using the pool at her new school.

Chapter twelve

The family went home just before the new term started. They had a few days in which to get Gabrielle's new uniform and visit the hospital in order to collect the new splint and raised-up shoe for her bad leg. She felt a bit self-conscious having to wear them, but she was very glad that she now didn't need to use her wheelchair all the time. The consultant at the hospital was very pleased with her and felt that she had made remarkable progress in the year since her accident.

The first day at St Anne's School was quite scary. The taxi came for her, and she felt very shy as she got out and entered the school gates. The new pupils started term one day before the rest of the school, and her form tutor was waiting at the door to welcome them.

'Hi, welcome to our school,' Mrs Banks said, 'Please tell me your name.' She had a list and was ticking off the names as she met the pupils.

'Gabrielle Price,' Gabby replied.

'That's great, Gabrielle. Come with me and I'll take you to the classroom.'

She led Gabrielle down a long corridor and into a sunny room.

'Find a seat wherever you like, and when everyone is here we'll introduce one another.'

Gabrielle found that about ten pupils were already in the classroom. As she looked around for a seat, a girl with long dark hair smiled at her and called her over.

'Why don't you sit with me?' she asked. 'By the way, my name's Claire.'

'I'm Gabrielle. Thank you, I'd like to sit with you.'

'It's really strange starting a new school, isn't it?' continued Claire. 'I live quite a way across the town, so not many of my friends from primary school are coming to St Anne's.'

'None of mine are coming here,' replied Gabrielle. 'I live quite a long way away too, but everyone thinks that this school will be the best for me because sometimes I need to use a wheelchair, and this school has such good facilities.'

New children kept coming into the room, and soon Mrs Banks joined them.

'I think everyone's here now,' she announced, 'so we'll start by doing the register. When I call your name, please stand up. That way we can see you and begin to get to know one another.'

Once the register had been called, Mrs Banks suggested that they all in turn get up and tell the class one thing about themselves and one reason why they had chosen St Anne's as their senior school. This really helped to break the ice. When it was Gabrielle's turn, she told everybody she had chosen this school because she had some injuries to her back and leg following an accident and that she was training so that one day, hopefully, she could be in the Paralympic swimming team.

Claire told them that she had chosen St Anne's because her elder sister was a pupil here. She came from a big family; she had five sisters and one brother.

The class gasped at that and one boy muttered, 'Poor guy: six sisters!' Everyone giggled. Claire said it was great fun belonging to a big family, and that her brother was spoilt rotten by all his older sisters!

When they had all finished telling the others about themselves, Mrs Banks talked to them about the school.

'In this school we have small classes and we try to be a family. This is a sports-specialist college, and lots of you have already told us that you have come here because you are good at a certain sport, or want eventually to work in the sport and leisure industry.

'I want to stress, right at the beginning, how important it is to look after one another and to be loyal to one another. Some of you have disabilities of various kinds. Take care of one another. Where you are strong, help those who are weaker. We all have some strong points and some weak ones. A couple of you are diabetic. If you need sugar or an insulin injection, you must be able to tell your friends and teachers, because we are here to help you.

'We are also very firm with bullies. If anyone is bullied for any reason, we want to know at once, because such things are not tolerated at St Anne's. It doesn't matter if it is one of the biggest pupils in the school who is doing the bullying; do not be afraid to tell us. We will help! Also, if in any circumstance you are offered drugs, alcohol or cigarettes, or if you see anyone carrying a weapon of any sort, we want to know. We are determined that this school will be a safe and happy environment for learning.'

Then she told them that she was going to take them on a tour of the school so that they could meet the various members of staff in the rooms where they taught, and also see the changing-rooms, the loos and get keys to the lockers where they could keep their personal things.

'It will be quite a long walk,' she said. 'Can you all manage?'

'I may be a bit slow,' said Gabrielle.

'That's fine,' answered her teacher. 'The rest of you, please make sure you don't leave Gabrielle behind.'

'I might need someone to push me into rooms,' a boy called Joe said. He had already told the class that he had a condition called spina bifida and his legs were paralysed. He could usually manage to propel his own wheelchair, but sometimes doorways were a bit difficult.

'Please also watch out for Joe and make sure he gets the help he needs,' said Mrs Banks. 'Bring everything with you. Don't ever leave personal belongings around in classrooms.'

It did seem a long tour, and Gabrielle wondered how she would ever remember where each class was held. Claire walked with her and whispered to her that her sister had said that it was OK—very quickly you found your way around the school. It was quite a modern building, and everywhere seemed light and bright.

Of course, the swimming pool was what Gabrielle wanted to see most of all, since she had not been able to visit the school last September, unlike most of the other pupils. It was a really big pool, and Gabrielle began to feel excited. Mr Black, her coach, had said that he would be

able to train her after school in the school pool, so long
as it could be fitted into the other activities held there.
Otherwise it might be arranged for her to come early to
school. He really wanted to increase her training to a
session each schoolday.

When the tour was over, the pupils locked their
belongings in their lockers and went out into the
grounds. It was all so different from primary school! The
playground there had always been full of children playing
running or skipping games, but this playground had no
hopscotch games marked out and no climbing frames to
play on; instead there was just bare tarmac, with a few
benches and picnic tables. Gabrielle's leg was aching
badly from walking round the school, so she headed
towards one of the benches. For a few minutes she felt
very alone and wished that Paula was there with her. She
felt some tears rising in her eyes, and quickly she told
herself to stop being so silly as she would soon feel at
home here.

Then she closed her eyes for a moment and asked God to
help her to be brave and to make friends.

When she opened her eyes she saw that Claire was
sitting beside her.

'Are you OK?' Claire asked.

'Yes, thank you—I'm just a bit tired. I'm not yet used to
walking very far,' Gabrielle answered.

'I've been to see what groups and clubs there are that
I can join,' said Claire. 'My sister Annie is in the upper
school and they have different clubs. I've put myself down
for the hockey group.' Then Claire added a little shyly, 'I
also want to join the Christian Union group. My family

are Christians and I became a Christian at a camp in the summer.'

Gabrielle looked at her in amazement. 'I didn't know there were groups like that! I'd like to go to that too, if I can. I have to have my swimming training each day, but as long as it doesn't clash, I would like to join. I'm a Christian too!'

Claire beamed at her. 'We're going to be such good friends!' she said. 'I'm so happy to have a Christian friend! God has really answered my prayers! I was a bit scared about coming to senior school, but now I feel so happy!'

'So do I!' replied Gabrielle. 'And so will my Granny Price when I tell her about you! One day you must meet my grandmother; she's so special, and she helps me to learn about God.'

So it was that Gabrielle made a new friend at senior school. Claire was a great help, too, and always made sure that her friend was not left behind. There were some days when Gabrielle's leg and back hurt so much she still needed her wheelchair.

The new lessons were challenging. At her primary school, Gabrielle had learnt some French, and Paul had helped her to learn a bit more, so that, although she had missed the trip to France with her class, she was well ahead with learning the language. Claire, however, had never learnt any French, so Gabrielle spent time in the lunch-break helping her. The girls did join the Christian Union, and, although some others in the class made fun of them and called them 'the God Squad', Gabrielle didn't mind at all because she found the group interesting, as well as a lot of fun.

Swimming training began in earnest once again. Mr Black was as good as his word and put her through her paces every day. Most days she stayed after school and trained for an hour and a half, and then the taxi arrived to take her home. On Fridays, however, the school pool was used by a group, so she was brought to school at 7 a.m. for her training session. Gabrielle could feel the freedom in the water and she knew that she was improving and getting very fast again. Mr Black was pleased with her. He could tell that she was really committed to training and that it was still her dream to win a gold medal!

Saturdays were always special. Paula usually came round to her house and they talked about school and helped each other with homework. Paula had made new friends, too, but, even so, she and Gabrielle were still as close friends as they had ever been, which Gabrielle was really pleased about. From time to time Claire would come over on a Saturday too, and the three of them could go ten-pin bowling with Dad and Paul. Amy was usually doing ballet. She loved it and was now taking exams and doing extremely well.

Gabrielle had taken to doing something else on a Saturday, too. When it was convenient, she went along to Granny Price's on Saturday evening and slept there overnight. They had such good times together, sipping hot chocolate and chatting over the events of the week. Gabrielle still liked to read the Bible stories with her grandmother, just as she had done before. They would also talk to God together about any problems or worries she had, or would just say 'thank you' for the week that had passed. Then on Sundays they went to church together.

Sometimes the rest of the family would be there too. Paula often came along now, just as she had promised to do when they left primary school.

Gabrielle loved her weekends and always went back to school on Monday with a new burst of energy. She was now making lots of friends at school, although her closest friend at St Anne's was still Claire. She found that most of her class were not only friendly, but also helpful to her with her disability. There was one awful day when, in the playground at break-time, a group of older boys and girls began to make fun of her and call her 'peg-leg'. They got her in a corner by the wall and started to kick her splint. They threatened her that, if she told tales about them, they would come after her every day, and she knew they could run faster than she could. Gabrielle was really frightened and began to shake, and the group then began to bully her even more. She couldn't get away from the group. Suddenly, she knew what she could do: her friend Jesus! She didn't close her eyes, but in her heart she just said, 'Lord Jesus, please help me!'

As she was silently crying out for help, a miracle happened! The PE master came around the corner, and the bullies were so intent on being horrible to Gabrielle that they didn't even notice Mr Spark's appearance on the scene.

'So, I've caught you at it at last!' Mr Spark said to the gang, who suddenly didn't look so big or so brave any more. 'I've had complaints about you before, and, as you well know, we do not tolerate any bullying in this school!' He was already making a list of the names of the culprits. 'I'll see you all in the staff-room at the end of the afternoon. If any of you fail to report to me, then it will be even worse for you! Now go to your classes!'

The gang slunk away.

Mr Spark turned to Gabrielle. 'Have they done this to you before?' he asked.

'No, sir,' she replied. Gabrielle was still shaking from her ordeal.

'Come with me, then, and I'll make sure you get to your own class without any more trouble. Am I right in thinking you are the Year 7 girl who's having swimming coaching?'

'Yes, sir, I am,' replied Gabrielle, as they walked towards the class door. 'I hope one day to make it to the Paralympics. I was training for the British squad before my accident.'

'Well, I have heard that you are doing very well in your training. This school will one day be very proud of you! Don't let those ignorant pupils put you off or upset you. They will be punished, and I doubt they will ever bother you again! If they do, you must come and tell me at once!'

'Thank you, sir, I will,' answered Gabrielle. 'Thank you for helping me today.'

'Off you go now, or you'll be late for your next class,' said Mr Spark, as Gabrielle opened the door to her classroom.

She went over to her desk, near where Claire was already sitting down.

'Are you OK?' Claire asked her. 'You look a bit upset.'

'I'm OK now,' Gabrielle answered, and then she told her friend what had happened, and how her prayer had been answered by a miracle.

'I bet no one has called Old Sparky a miracle before!' giggled Claire.

Chapter thirteen

One afternoon, Gabrielle was coming out of the changing-rooms, ready for her coaching session, when she heard voices. One voice was Mr Black's, but she didn't recognize the other. Mr Black was waiting for her by the side of the pool and with him was a lady she didn't know.

'Gabrielle, this is Frances Brown,' he said. 'She's from the ASA, the Amateur Swimming Association, and I hope you don't mind, but she's going to sit in on your session today.'

Gabrielle said 'hello' politely and smiled at Frances. 'That's OK,' she said, and she dived into the pool, ready to begin her training.

The session went very much as usual and Mr Black was pleased with her times as she swam lengths in breast-stroke and freestyle. When they had finished and she got out of the pool to go and change, the lady gave her a beaming smile and congratulated her on her progress. She asked a little about the accident and then told Gabrielle to hold on to her hopes and dreams.

The following week, Mr Black showed Gabrielle a letter which he had received from Frances Brown.

*'Your pupil, Gabrielle Price, shows exceptional ability
in the pool. There is no doubt in my mind that she
should be selected for the British Paralympic squad.
I shall put forward a recommendation to that effect.
She will probably need to come to Sheffield to compete
against other possible Paralympians.*

'Yours sincerely,
'Frances Brown.'

'Wow!' said Gabrielle. 'Am I getting that good?'

'You are indeed, and I'm really proud of you,' replied Mr
Black. 'But don't let this go to your head! There's still a
lot of hard training you need to do before you can compete
against others in the squad. If I may, I'll phone your
parents tonight and we can talk about arranging a trip to
Sheffield in the near future.'

'Thank you,' Gabrielle said to her coach. 'But I know
that my sister, Amy, has a ballet exam soon, so it would be
best if the trip was after that.'

'Well, I'll talk to your folks and we'll fix something up,'
said Mr Black, as he saw Gabrielle into her taxi to go home.

As always, Gabrielle's coach was as good as his word and
he phoned her parents that evening. He sounded excited as
he spoke to Mr and Mrs Price.

'Can you allow her to go to Sheffield soon?' he
asked. 'I could be free to be there with her in the next
school holidays.'

'Well, I'm sure we can manage it one way or another.
One of us will go with her. Please let me have a day or two
so that I can make arrangements,' replied Mr Price.

That evening, Granny Price came round for a chat with

her son, as she so often did. The children were always pleased to see her and soon had her involved in a game of Monopoly. As usual, Paul won, but nobody minded. Dad laughed and said that maybe Paul should be a property developer when he grew up!

After Paul, Gabrielle and Amy had said goodnight and gone up to bed, Mr and Mrs Price discussed with Granny the trip to Sheffield. It was almost Christmas, and so, if Gabrielle was to go in the next school holidays, it would mean a lot of changes to the plans they had already made for Christmas.

'The good thing is,' said Mr Price, 'I've already got leave from Christmas until after New Year, so I would be free to take her, but she really needs a woman to look after her in the hotel. She's getting to be a young lady now.'

'I wonder,' Granny Price was thinking out loud, 'I wonder if Jenny could help. Jen is coming down for Christmas and has several days off from work.'

Mr Price thought it would be an excellent idea if his sister could help with the trip. Auntie Jenny had always been a great favourite of the children. She was a nurse who worked at a hospital in the Midlands.

'I want to phone her tonight about something else, so I'll ask her then,' said Granny Price. 'If she can't help, then I'll go with Gabrielle and take care of her, but it would be better if Jenny could do it.'

Soon all the arrangements were made for Gabrielle, her father and Auntie Jenny, along with Mr Black her coach, to go to Sheffield on 27 December for a few days.

Christmas was such an exciting time that Gabrielle didn't think very much about the trip until the day they were packing and getting ready to go. She could hardly believe that it was really happening! Auntie Jenny was full of enthusiasm, and was as excited as if she herself was going to the Paralympic trials! The hospital where she worked had stopped doing any major surgery over the Christmas and New Year holidays, and many of the wards were closed for cleaning, so there was no problem with her asking for a few extra days off to help her niece.

One of the first things that happened at Sheffield was that Gabrielle was examined by a doctor, who assessed her disability. Then he decided which category she should be given for her swimming. It was very comforting for Gabrielle to have Auntie Jenny there when the doctor asked lots of questions and used many long words. She was told she would be S9, SB8 and SM9, whatever that meant!

After she had seen the doctor, the real fun began! The pool was magnificent, and it was so good to swim alongside other competitors who had similar problems to those she had. It was hard work, but Gabrielle had never minded that. She felt exhilarated by all the exercise. It was soon obvious to everyone that she was very good and certainly a Paralympic hopeful. Although she did not win every race, she did win several, and she was only a few seconds behind the winners in the races she lost. She could tell that Mr Black was very pleased with her.

Dad had gone back home after driving them all to Sheffield, but it was great fun having Auntie Jenny as her helper. She was always laughing and was full of funny stories, which made Gabrielle laugh until she cried! In the evenings they sometimes went out to eat in a restaurant, and one night they went to the cinema to see a Disney film. It made the whole week seem like a special treat, and Gabrielle was sorry when it was all over.

Before the end of the week the selectors had a meeting with Mr Black to try to plan Gabrielle's future training. They decided that it was time for her to start swimming in major races at home and abroad, at national, European and international level, so that she would be ready for the next Paralympic games.

When her dad arrived to drive them back home, he was also called into a meeting and told about Gabrielle's prospects. Once again he was asked how the family would manage.

'I'm not sure—we'll just take each event as it comes; but don't worry, we will make sure that she can compete,' he promised. 'Somehow, we will do it. My firm is very understanding and, because of her disability, it has agreed to sponsor her swimming. This will help with the costs involved. We are all so proud of our Gabrielle!'

Saying goodbye to Auntie Jenny was hard. They had been having so much fun together. Auntie Jenny made a promise to Gabrielle: 'I'll try to get time off to be with you for competitions whenever I can.' Jenny looked at Mr Price, her brother. 'I'm actually thinking of having a sabbatical soon. Maybe I can work it so that I'm free for the Paralympics, so that I can be Gabby's attendant. I think they may need a nurse around to help with some of the athletes. Some of them have such severe disabilities, but they are so courageous!'

Chapter fourteen

Gabrielle found it quite hard to go back to school after all the excitement of Christmas and the Paralympic trials. However, it was really good to see Claire again, as well as her other school friends. At the Christian Union meeting they talked about their holidays and Gabrielle told them all about the trials. Everyone was so encouraging. It was very hard work training and also doing her school-work to the best of her ability. Each day she also tried to spend some time reading her Bible and praying. Her life was so busy, but she knew she must not push her best Friend of all, Jesus, to one side.

As she had been promised, she was entered into various competitions. Each time, she told her friends in the CU and they promised to pray for her. At assembly her achievements were always announced, especially if she won a medal. As the school was a sports academy, many of the pupils were excelling in different sports and the school teams did very well, so Gabrielle didn't feel too embarrassed when her achievements were talked about. Her classmates were proud of her, and they usually looked out for her and helped her whenever she needed it. Soon her wheelchair was discarded for ever, and no one even noticed her limp any more. If she needed time off school for a competition, she had to make up the lessons that she had missed, and Claire helped her with this.

There was one time when she had to go to Paris for a competition. Auntie Jenny had taken time off work to go with her. They crossed the English Channel by going underneath it and through the Channel Tunnel in a high-speed train. Gabrielle was so excited. She remembered the time when she was at primary school and had had to miss the class trip to Paris, and how her grandmother had told her that one day she might go to Paris and win a gold medal! And now she was actually going there for a European competition!

It was a very exciting competition, and, although Gabrielle didn't win the gold, she lost by only a fraction of a second and won silver! She was delighted with her silver medal, and, as she stood on the rostrum to receive it, she whispered a 'thank you' to Jesus for being with her and helping her.

The Olympic year dawned. In England it was snowy and cold, and Gabrielle found it very hard to get up early and get to the pool, but winning the European silver spurred Gabrielle on. She was determined to win gold! As the winter months turned to spring, so the pressure of training increased. How glad Gabrielle was that she had such a supportive family! As the time for the Paralympic Games drew near, they all helped and encouraged her. She was excused helping with jobs at home so that she could concentrate on her swimming. Granny Price often drove her to the different venues to which she had to go, so that her dad didn't miss too much work.

Auntie Jenny had taken a nine months' sabbatical from work and had moved back into her old bedroom at Granny Price's house so that she could help in any way. Amy and Paul were quite sure that Gabrielle was going to win, and they told everybody they knew that she would be a gold medallist. Gabrielle was determined not to let them down! She knew that she had the best times for her group in the British squad, but there was some tough opposition out there on the world scene!

When it was time for the team to leave and go to the Olympic camp in Hong Kong, she was so pleased to have Auntie Jenny at her side. The whole family hoped to fly out after the heats if she made it to the finals. Mr Black said that her achievement was the pinnacle of his career; if she won, he would retire a happy man!

Gabrielle felt that she would disappoint everyone she knew if she did not make it to the finals. Every night she prayed that she would do her very best and not make any mistakes. She also asked God to calm her nerves and help her to sleep, because she was so tense.

It was fantastic living in the Olympic village. Gabrielle was so proud of her fellow-athletes, many of whom had severe disabilities and were very brave. Her own back and leg problems seemed so slight in comparison.

The heats went well, and Gabrielle won almost every time, even recording a new personal best time. Auntie Jenny was as excited as she was, as she realized that her niece really did have a chance, not only to be in the breast-stroke final, but maybe even to win a medal.

'I'm through to the final!' Gabrielle shouted down the phone to her mum after two days of heats.

'We're so very, very pleased for you, and proud of you, darling!' Mum joyfully replied. 'We'll all be there, cheering you on. Even the Patels are coming out, including Saffron!'

The night before the finals, Gabrielle asked God especially to keep her calm and help her to sleep, and also to help her not to be too disappointed if she did not get a medal. The competition was very stiff and she had only a slim chance. The weather was also very hot and humid, and, with all the excitement as well, it was not easy to get to sleep. As she lay in her bed, she thought again of the Bible verse her grandmother had given to her several years ago, from Jeremiah 29 verse 11: 'I know the plans I have for you … plans to prosper you and not to harm you, plans to give you hope and a future.' She thought back to the accident, when it had seemed as if all her plans were wrecked and she had thought she had no future, but would just be a cripple.

'Thank you, God, that whether I win or lose, you have done so much for me, and I love you!' she prayed, and then she drifted off to sleep.

The next day the contestants all stood by the pool, lined up for their race. It was the final! Gabrielle had drawn a good lane. Her tummy had been turning over and over and she had been to the loo so many times, but now she suddenly felt full of peace. The instant the starting gun sounded she dived, a fantastic dive that gave her just that little lead she needed. Her mind now concentrated only on her strokes. Power flowed into her arms and her one good leg, and she felt that she was swimming as never before. Her turns went well, and she pulled just a little ahead, although she herself was not aware of that. All she was aware of was her stroke, strong and powerful.

Suddenly, it was all over and she touched the pool's edge to the sound of cheers and shouts. She had won! She had won the gold for Britain! She had won the gold for her country, her family, her school, Mr Black, but, most of all, for Jesus!

As the other competitors hugged and congratulated her, tears of joy and thankfulness sprang into her eyes. With a Union Jack wrapped around her, she made her way to the podium and stood on the centre dais. A girl presented her with a bouquet—and then the gold medal was placed around her neck! She turned as the flag was raised above her head and the National Anthem, 'God Save our Gracious Queen', was played.

Weeping with pure joy, pride and thankfulness, Gabrielle Price stood there, gold medallist of the Paralympic Games, and she whispered, 'Thank you, God!'

About Day One:

Day One's threefold commitment:

~ To be faithful to the Bible, God's inerrant, infallible Word;

~ To be relevant to our modern generation;

~ To be excellent in our publication standards.

I continue to be thankful for the publications of Day One. They are biblical; they have sound theology; and they are relevant to the issues at hand. The material is condensed and manageable while, at the same time, being complete—a challenging balance to find. We are happy in our ministry to make use of these excellent publications.

JOHN MACARTHUR, PASTOR-TEACHER,
GRACE COMMUNITY CHURCH, CALIFORNIA

It is a great encouragement to see Day One making such excellent progress. Their publications are always biblical, accessible and attractively produced, with no compromise on quality. Long may their progress continue and increase!

JOHN BLANCHARD, AUTHOR, EVANGELIST AND APOLOGIST

Visit our website for more information and to request a free catalogue of our books.

www.dayone.co.uk